The White Continent
The Story of Antarctica

Thomas R. Henry

The White Continent

The Story of Antarctica

WILLIAM SLOANE ASSOCIATES

Publishers   *New York*

Typography and format designed by

LEONARD W. BLIZARD

W

Manufactured in the United States of America

Published simultaneously in Canada by George J. McLeod,
Ltd., Toronto

To JEAN

Preface

This may be the last generation of terrestrial explorers. During the past half-century the number of unvisited places on the face of this planet has been reduced to almost zero. Already scientists have predicted moon landings before the end of the century, and the adventurous imagination has begun to turn toward outer space.

With one major exception, only the peaks of the highest mountains and the floors of the deepest seas on earth still are unattained. The exception consists of at least three million square miles of the world's land surface around the South Pole. The green-skyed, white continent at the bottom of the earth is geography's greatest unknown. It is a place of unearthly beauty, majesty, and mystery, and still —despite the technological developments which have taken much of the danger and hardship from exploration—a place of infinite challenge to man's hardiness and courage.

The reasons for its persistence as a mystery-haunted region are various. It is isolated beyond stormy seas, ramparts of ice, and nearly impassable mountains. The land is essentially uninhabitable. Its economic and strategic values are debatable. Yet the Antarctic is certain to be of constantly increasing public interest as world powers wrangle for titles of empire in the dead wilderness, set up semi-permanent military stations on its edges, and slowly penetrate more and more of its interior. As this is written, two major exploring expeditions are on the continent and seven "forts" have been established.

The dead continent with its surrounding seas and islands is the subject of extensive literature, consisting largely of scientific treatises and journals of personal adventure. The intent of the present volume is different from that of the treatise or the journal. It has been written in the hope that it will enable the reader to share with the explorer something of the ineffable physical, mental, and emotional experience which comes to all who cross the borders of a region that differs so notably from any other on earth.

Historically the Antarctic has been the scene of some of the greatest of human adventures, tragedies, and triumphs. The sagas of Scott, Amundsen, and Shackleton are incorporated because they seem to give a human soul to this dead land which spurns life.

The writer's personal experience in the Antarctic was during the winter of 1946–47 as a magazine correspondent with the U. S. Navy expedition "High Jump," under the command of Rear Admirals Richard E. Byrd and Richard H. Cruzen. This was by far the most ambitious project as yet undertaken for exploration of the Far South. The expedition entered the iceberg-filled waters below the Antarctic Circle with twelve ships and approximately four thousand officers and men—a larger personnel than all previous expeditions combined. Its primary mission was the accurate mapping of the continental shoreline and the mountains that form the rim of the continent. Its discoveries nearly doubled man's geographic knowledge of Antarctica.

The Byrd-Cruzen operation was a luxury cruise in the light of the hardships and perils of previous expeditions. It had at its command all the technical developments in aviation and exploration that came about during the last months of the war, many of which—never used in combat —were like swords turned into ploughshares. They included such equipment as aviation photographic units capable of mapping hundreds of square miles on a single day and the incredible magnetometer which mapped terrain buried under thousands of feet of ice. In addition there was a superabundance of everything that could add to personal comfort, from ice goggles to cigarettes. This was steam-heated exploring.

Even so, to all who accompanied it, the expedition was a great adventure. The men of the group sailed and flew over the world's last frontiers; they found themselves in the midst of a landscape incomparable with that of any other region on this planet and nearly indescribable in terms of familiar sights and sounds.

There was no lack of danger. Within a week after entering the Ross ice pack it was necessary to rescue the submarine that accompanied the task force from menacing icebergs and escort it to the safety of open water. Long before the pack was cleared gaping holes appeared in the hull of the command ship *Mount Olympus*, and one of the exploring planes had crashed into a mountainside. Killer whales, most fearsome of extant monsters, gathered hungrily and expectantly in the wake of the ships.

The thrill of such experiences is unavoidably reflected in these pages. The expedition is necessarily the source of much of the color and sentiment, but the book is intended to embrace an inclusive picture of Antarctica's human and natural history.

THOMAS R. HENRY

Contents

Contents

Map Drawing by Rafael Palacios

The White Continent
The Story of Antarctica

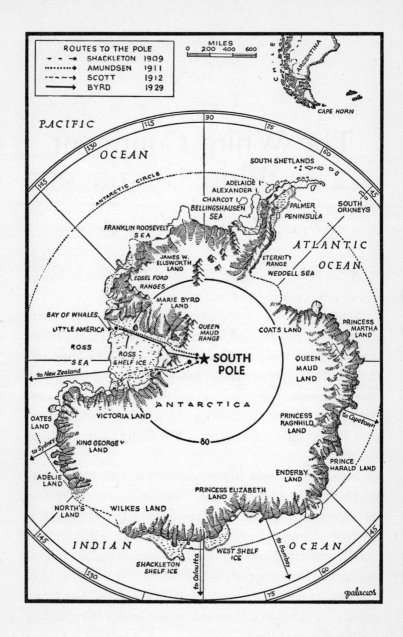

The White Continent

A dead continent lies swathed in a mile-thick shroud of ice at the bottom of the world.

Storms and cold of a hundred million year-long winters have woven this sheet of intricate patterns and many colors around what was once a country of green swamps and forests. Dinosaurs probably roamed its marshes and primitive mammals lurked in its woodlands. No man's eye ever looked on its wild landscape; the weaving of the shroud had started millenniums before the first human appeared on earth.

Now there is only lifeless desolation with white, pink, and blue mountains rising like tombstones over the surface of an endless, glittering white desert. The landscape is that of a cosmic graveyard. At least two-thirds of it is totally unknown, and of that part—mainly the coastline—which has been mapped, most of it has been seen only in fleeting glimpses through cloud rifts from fast-flying planes. Fewer than a thousand human beings have set foot on the continent itself.

This is the Antarctic Continent. It is a land mass about the size of the United States and Australia combined—fifth largest of the continents with a roughly calculated area of five and one-half million square miles compared with seven million for South America. It is approximately circular in shape, but with a narrow projection, the Palmer Peninsula, extending northward toward South America.

The continent might be compared to a titanic bowl with a chipped rim, its vast ice plateau bordered for at least two-thirds of its circumference by nearly continuous ranges of high mountains through whose passes gigantic rivers of ice spill into the seas.

Antarctica is the highest of the continents. The average elevation of the interior is more than 7,500 feet above sea level, higher than all but the loftiest crests of the Appalachians. It is a continent in the sky, as anyone who has tried to fly over it can testify. In almost the geometric center is the South Pole, the southernmost point on earth where all meridians merge and the only direction is north.

This is the world's coldest land. Even on the sea's edge in midsummer the temperature seldom rises above zero centigrade, with the average for the year at least 40 degrees below that of the lands nearest the North Pole. There are two major reasons for this—first, the elevation, with the resulting thinness of the atmosphere over the south polar plateau; second, the bottom of the world is land, while the top of the world is water which absorbs, retains, and re-radiates heat.

The difference in temperature between the two poles is the difference between life and death, for the Arctic, even in winter, is a region of abundant life and the beaches of its islands become fairyland lawns of flowers during the brief summer. Musk-oxen graze in lush pastures of the farthest northlands in the world; insects are so abundant that at times they make life unendurable for the traveler. But plant life, for all its tricks of wind-blown spores and seeds, cannot get a foothold in Antarctic lands. Even in those rare spots where the surface of the continent is free of ice there is so little soil and the temperature so seldom rises above freezing that seeds have no chance to germinate. Without plants there can, of course, be no permanent animal life, for the magical properties of chlorophyll in green leaves are essential for animal existence. So life here, with very few exceptions, exists only at the edge of the seas.

The continent of Antarctica is in the middle of an ice age—its desolation is perhaps not unlike what a visitor from another world would have found in parts of Europe or North America during any of the great glaciations. In fact, a journey into the interior of Antarctica today might be likened to a time-ship voyage into ten million years ago. But there is one great difference: Life never was brought to a complete standstill in the Northern Hemisphere. Animals and plants retreated before the creeping walls of ice; through hundreds of generations they adjusted themselves to new ways of living. Here escape was cut off in all directions by deep and stormy seas.

The dead land may be a preview of the entire planet millions of years from now when the heat from a slowly cooling sun no longer is enough for life to continue and a thickening shell of ice is formed around the globe. Long before then the last men will have perished of cold and hunger.

The ancient history of Antarctica is almost entirely a matter of speculation. At one time in the past—perhaps at several times—large parts of the continent enjoyed a temperate, or even semi-tropical, climate, as is evidenced by the remains of abundant life in its rocks. Yet there is no reason to believe that the lands actually at the bottom of the world were ever appreciably warmer than they are at present. Here, then, is one of the great conundrums of geology for which only one theory seems to offer a remotely acceptable explanation. The theory begins with the assumption, for which there is considerable evidence, that about 200 million years ago most of the land now in the Southern Hemisphere was in one super-continent, Gondwanaland. This was during the Permian geological age, one of the great transition periods in history. The earth at this time was flat and swampy; much of it was covered with gigantic tree ferns and club mosses which eventually were embedded in the black ooze to form coal deposits. The earliest backboned land animals—big, slimy amphibians like present-day salamanders—came out of the sea and led a precarious existence in the low-lying marshes; the first reptiles, ancestors of the dinosaurs, were coming into existence.

During millenniums of this age thick ice sheets lay over large sections of Gondwanaland, covering what are now equatorial Africa and South America. Enormous glaciers flowed from lands at present on the equator toward lands which are now around the South Pole. At that time what is now the Antarctic Continent was warm and green; parts of it may not have differed greatly from the basins of the Amazon or Congo today.

The late Permian and the succeeding geological era, the Triassic, when the dinosaurs were starting their long reign as lords of creation, were periods of great earth upheavals. The slumbering planet suffered convulsions in a nightmare of earthquakes and hot lava. Mountains were born and swift rivers drained the green-scummed swamps into the seas. Somewhere during this time Gondwanaland apparently exploded. The major fragments were Africa, South America, part of India, Australia, New Zealand, and Antarctica. Before the great explosion the enormous land mass had drifted like a raft on a sea of underlying plastic rock across the bottom of the earth so that lands now at the equator were at the South Pole and the dead continent of today, together with New Zealand and Australia, was in a relatively temperate zone. But the drift continued and sometime before the final explosive fracture the land now constituting Antarctica had come to rest roughly in its present position.

This explanation, of course, is only tentative; it has its enthusiastic advocates, and equally fervent opponents, among geologists and paleontologists. But it is a bold effort to provide some sort of explanation for a number of paradoxes. Why was the Antarctic Continent a place of luxurious vegetation when central Africa was covered with ice? Why was this vegetation, the characteristic growth of which was a fernlike plant known as "glossopteris," common during the Permian age to all the lands of the Southern Hemisphere? Why did glaciers apparently flow from the equator to the South Pole? Stamped on the rocks everywhere around the equator and southward is the mystic signature of Gondwanaland, the fossil imprint of the glossopteris leaf—presumably a semi-tropical plant. How could it have spread over lands so widely separated as those which occupy the Southern Hemisphere today? Also the contours of these lands fit roughly together like pieces of a jigsaw puzzle—closely enough to admit the hypothesis that they might once have been joined.

There are alternatives to the continental drift theory. Attempts have been made to explain the climatic phenomenon by the shifting of the axis of the earth. But even in a billion years this shift is slight—certainly not enough to place the South Pole in central Africa. Still another hypothesis is that the crust of the earth is a thin, loose shell which slips and slides around the denser, underlying rock layers. The geology of the Northern Hemisphere offers evidence in support of this theory. Within the past few years specialists of the Carnegie Institution of Washington have found abnormalities of "fossil magnetism"— the inclination to the horizontal of magnetic particles embedded in rock—for which a logical explanation is that areas of the present Maryland and Pennsylvania once were in the approximate position of Basutoland.

The reasons for the backward and forward shufflings of ice, common to both Northern and Southern hemispheres, are far from clear. Perhaps the most widely accepted theory is that the advances northward and southward from the poles take place, paradoxically enough, when the earth gets warmer. This results in greater precipitation, which falls over the poles as snow. The additional weight pressing on the ice causes it to flow in all directions, gaining momentum as more and more pressure is built up. Thus an ice age waxes until the earth gets colder again, with a resulting decline in precipitation and pressure. Then the glaciers start to melt at their forward edges, and there is a progressively accelerated recession toward the poles. These major changes in climate, perhaps due to fluctuations in the heat received from the sun, may occur several times in the course of a million years, but they are hardly sufficient to change tropics to ice sheets.

Thus the existence of a semi-tropical vegetation over parts of Antarctica about 200 million years ago remains one of the great unsolved mysteries of geology. Very likely the clue to its solution lies buried for all the time of man in the rocks under the continental icecap.

It is quite improbable that the continent has been entirely free of ice the past 100 million years, although there may have been several advances and recessions of the ice in the intervening millenniums. Edges of the continent certainly have been tree-covered and may have had a climate as moderate as that of southern Canada today. On the Palmer Peninsula, the farthest extension of Antarctica toward the temperate zone, British geologists have found fossil imprints of sequoia leaves of a species similar to those which grew on the Pacific Coast of the United States about twenty million years ago. Such trees would have required fairly temperate climatic conditions and a plentiful rainfall, thus bringing parts of Antarctica as habitable lands well within the age of mammals. The fact remains, however, that only one vertebrate fossil has been found in continental rocks—that of a primitive fish.

Still, it is highly probable that there were primitive mammals, flowering plants, and birds in the great sequoia forests on the rim of Antarctica. The continent may, in fact, have formed a bridge between Australasia and South America for the marsupial mammals represented by the opossum in the Western Hemisphere. If mammal fossils ever are found under the ice they are most likely to be those of creatures of the general kangaroo-opossum order.

The probability of some sort of a land bridge between the Antarctic Continent and Australia is evidenced by plant distribution, of which wild tobacco is one of the best examples. It grows in three continents—North and South America, and Australia—and beyond much question it originated within the last twenty million years in South America. The only likely road it could have followed in its migration to Australia is around the rim of Antarctica, where it would have required a fairly equable climate to survive a migration that probably extended over a millennium.

It is natural to speculate whether primitive man existed on this continent when it was alive, but the possibility is very small indeed since Antarctica has doubtlessly been covered with ice for much longer than the two or three million years that any animals resembling human beings have been on earth. The closest approach to man that might have existed in a habitable southern continent before this time would have been similar to some of the ape monsters whose fossilized bones have been found in South Africa. The dead land has been far off the road of the evolution of modern man, and probably of any of the placental animals. No mammals existed in New Zealand before the coming of man there about a thousand years ago, and in Australia few except pouched creatures of the generalized kangaroo family were to be found. The Antarctic Continent belonged to the same general complex of lands, but was even more remote than the others from the major theaters of mammalian development.

There are some indications, difficult to evaluate, that the great ice sheet again is retreating. Only a few million years from now a resurrection of the dead continent may take place, when its hills will be green again and its mountains filled with the roar of falling waters. For cycles of geological history repeat themselves—springtimes of the ages inevitably follow winters of the ages. The earth wobbles on its axis, its shell of light rock slips and slides around its heavy center, the heat of the sun undergoes considerable fluctuations over millenniums. Any one of these phenomena would be sufficient to cause notable recessions of the ice, and if two or three of them coincided the great Antarctic glaciation might come to an end.

Such an occurrence will spell doom for much of the rest of the earth. The levels of the oceans will be raised several hundred feet by the melting polar cap and the present most heavily populated regions, including many of the world's largest cities, will be on sea bottom. It has been estimated that New York, for example, will be submerged under three hundred feet of water. However, scientists doubt that the human race will have persisted until that day comes.

Thus Antarctica stands like a menacing white ogre. Sheltered valleys clear of ice have been found on the continent—in summer there are a few open water lakes—and here and there mosses and lichens have been discovered matted on the faces of ledges. Great clouds of smoke filled with corrosive gases pour from the crater of Mount

Erebus, the dead continent's only active volcano, indicating thermal activity under the earth's surface. Stark mountain peaks bear unmistakable marks showing that they once were buried under ice.

But the menace of the white continent looms afar; for the present it is a land of mystery and adventure. Almost anywhere one goes in Antarctica he is where man has never been before. It is a place for the making of new heroes, a door ajar into a near infinity of mystery, beauty, glory, and danger.

Sealed Orders

The idea of a southern continent has persisted since man first recognized that his planet was a sphere, for a great land mass at the bottom of the world was considered necessary to maintain the balance of the globe in space. Before actual exploration of the Antarctic, fancy ran wild; the popular picture of this continent was of a fertile, thickly inhabited land. Alexander Dalrymple, the learned eighteenth-century hydrographer of the East India Company, stirred the British imagination by the prediction that the population probably would exceed fifty millions. There was little realization of the intense cold in the far south—scientists shared with schoolchildren the naïve assumption that the temperature was higher south of the equator.

Early in 1768 the naval bark *Endeavour* left England on one of the most significant exploring expeditions in history. Its ostensible purpose was the transport of astronomers to observe the transit of the planet Venus in Tahiti, but just before sailing the *Endeavour*'s commander, Lieutenant James Cook, then at the outset of his career as one of the greatest explorers in history, was given secret orders. A copy of these orders was discovered in the Admiralty archives a few years ago.

After the astronomers had been set ashore, Cook's instructions read, the *Endeavour* was to sail directly southward to the reputed polar continent. There the commander was ordered "to observe the nature of the soil and the products thereof, the beasts and fowls that inhabit or frequent it, the fish that are to be found in the rivers or on the coast and in what plenty; and in case you find any mines, minerals, or valuable stones you are to bring home specimens of each, as also such specimens of the seeds, fruits, and grains as you may be able to collect. You are likewise to observe the genius, temper, disposition, and number of the natives and endeavour by all proper means to cultivate a friendship and alliance with them, making presents of such trifles as they may value and inviting them to traffic. . . ."

Secrecy was essential, since Spain and France also had designs on the undiscovered continent. Hostilities had threatened between Great Britain and Spain in 1765 when Admiral Byron, grandfather of the poet, annexed the Falkland Islands off southern Argentina. The Spanish crown had considered these islands a possible gateway to the rich lands around the South Pole. Spain, in fact, had laid claim to the hypothetical southern continent more than two centuries earlier; in 1539 Emperor Charles V appointed a worthy named Pedro Sancho de Hoz governor of "all the lands which are on the other sides of the Straits" of Magellan, as a reward for his services in the conquest of Peru. Spanish maps showed the continent as a vast territory stretching from the tip of South America across the pole to the "Kingdom of China." The Breton nobleman, Yves de Kerguelen, scouting South Atlantic waters for the great land mass at the bottom of the world, in 1772 discovered the curious cabbage-covered island which now bears his name. Disappointed, he had named it Desolation Island.

Cook followed orders exactly on his 1768 voyage. He failed to find the expected continent, but he explored and claimed for the British crown the eastern coast of Australia. The Earl of Sandwich, First Lord of the Admiralty, was determined that the cross of Saint George would fly over the South Pole in his lifetime, and four years later Cook again was dispatched to the South Pacific with orders to push his two ships southward as far as the pole —if he did not sooner discover the continent—and to circumnavigate the globe in high southern latitudes. Cook succeeded in reaching latitude 71 south, where he faced an impenetrable wall of ice. For months he skirted the white barrier without finding an opening. He and nearly all his men fell sick on the ration of salted meat and mouldy biscuits and he was forced reluctantly to turn northward, satisfied that if any southern continent existed it was uninhabited and probably uninhabitable.

It remained for a twenty-one-year-old Connecticut boy to discover the continent nearly a half-century after Cook's second voyage. Despite his youth, the boy was captain of a ship that sailed below the circle in the late south polar spring of 1820. His name was Nathaniel Brown Palmer and in his honor the northern peninsula of Antarctica is designated on most American maps as Palmer Land.

This boy's claim to one of the major geographical discoveries of all time was no accident. Palmer was an explorer with the assigned job of finding new lands. He was master of the forty-five-ton sloop *Hero*—forty-seven feet long with a sixteen-foot beam—only a little larger than an ordinary cabin cruiser of the present. He was necessarily a skilled seaman and an expert navigator . . . perhaps it would be better to say that he was an instinctive navigator, for he steered his little craft, manned by five grizzled New England sailors, through driving snow in the world's most perilous waters where no stars shone.

Even at twenty, Palmer was an experienced Antarctic explorer. The year before, he had shipped as second mate on the sealing brig *Hersilia* which set out for the fabled Aurora Islands, believed to be somewhere south of Cape Horn. It was rumored through the New England sealing ports that the breeding rookeries of all the fur seals in the Far South lay there, and any ship that succeeded in reaching the islands would return with an inestimable wealth of pelts. The location was a British secret, but young Palmer picked up a tip from a drunken English sailor when the *Hersilia* put in at the Falkland Islands for provisions. He guided the ship to the great seal rookeries of the South Shetlands, where the bloody fur harvest broke all records.

The old seaport of Stonington, Connecticut, was wildly excited when the *Hersilia* returned. Here, it seemed, was the prospect of wealth for every seafaring family in town; Nathaniel Palmer was the hero of the hour. A fleet of several ships was outfitted to sail for the seal islands the next year, under the command of Captain Benjamin

Pendleton. The smallest of these craft was the *Hero*, which had been especially built to serve as the scout of the fleet. By common consent the twenty-year-old-boy was placed in command. Palmer's job was to hunt among the icebergs in his small, easily maneuvered ship for new seal islands while the crews of the other ships were engaged in slaughtering and skinning the animals of one rookery.

From the South Shetlands the *Hero* pushed southward into unknown seas. What happened then is recounted in Palmer's dairy as quoted many years later by his niece, the late Mrs. Richard Fanning Loper of Stonington:

I pointed the bow of the little craft to the south-ward and with her wings spread, main sail abeam, and jib abreast the opposite bow, she speeded on her way to new sealing grounds like a thing of life and light. With her flowing sheet she seemed to enter into the spirit which possessed my ambition. She flew along the wave and over billow until she brought us in sight of land not laid down on my chart. I cruised for several days in order to satisfy myself it was not an island. I ran into several bays without meeting seals, and headed northward, drifting along under heavy canvas, "laying to" at night which consumed the majority of the day, most of the time the mist so dense that I could not see the lookout on the fore-castle.

This was sometime between November 15 and 21, 1820, according to the calculations of Professor William H. Hobbs of the University of Michigan. Palmer had found his new land, from his own sun observations at about latitude 63.45 south and longitude 60 west.

A distinguished contemporary witness of unquestionable veracity, Admiral Fabian von Bellingshausen of the Imperial Russian Navy, substantiated Palmer's claim. With an exploring fleet of two corvettes, acting on special orders of Tzar Alexander I, he had been sailing for two years along the edge of the ice pack in a vain attempt to break through to the southward and raise the Russian flag over the fabled southern continent.

Bellingshausen, a man of the utmost integrity and a navigator of exceptional skill, had made many significant contributions to Antarctic geography. Twice his two ships, the *Vostok* and the *Mirny*, had crossed the circle. The Admiral had discovered the vast and impenetrable sea of icebergs and mirages which now bears his name. He had bestowed the name of his sovereign on one of the largest of the Antarctic islands which was not to be explored for more than a century. But in his major objective he had failed; the thick ice pack had been an insuperable barrier. Although Bellingshausen never actually saw the continent his voyage is the basis of all present Russian claims to Antarctic territory. His manuscript report was resurrected from the accumulated dust of more than 125 years in naval archives and published by the Soviet government, apparently without change, two years ago.

Heartsick with disappointment and fearful of the reception he would receive when he reported to the Tzar, the Admiral was on his way home when he met the *Hero* and received from Palmer a report of his discoveries. Palmer wrote in his diary:

I gave him the latitude and longitude of my lowest point. He rose much agitated, begging I would reproduce my log book and chart, with which request I complied and a boat was sent for it. When they were laid on the table he examined them carefully without comment, then rose from his seat saying:

"What do I see and what do I hear from a boy in his teens—that he is commander of a tiny boat the size of the launch of my frigate, has pushed his way to the pole through storm and ice, and reached the point I, in command of one of the best-appointed fleets at the disposal of my august master, have for three long, weary, anxious years sought day and night for."

With his hand on my head, he added:

"What shall I say to my master? What will he think of me? Be that as it may, my grief is your joy. Wear your laurels with my sincere prayers for your welfare. I name the land you have discovered in honor of yourself, noble boy, Palmer's Land."

Ten years later Palmer made his last Antarctic cruise as captain of the brig *Annawan*, flagship of an exploring expedition of three vessels financed by himself and several other Stonington sealers. The purpose was "to search for lands in still unvisited waters." The costs were to be met by sealing. However, the expedition met with bad luck from the start. When the vessels arrived at the South Shetlands early in 1830 the Antarctic summer was nearly over; snowstorm followed snowstorm and blizzard chased blizzard; ice formed on the decks so fast the ships were in danger of floundering. No new lands were discovered.

This expedition would be of no significance if the announced objectives were the actual ones. There is reason to question this, however, because of the presence on board the *Annawan* of a certain Jeremiah N. Reynolds, listed in the ship's roster as a "scientist." It is quite possible—although it is difficult to picture a man of Palmer's common sense involved in such an enterprise—that this expedition was a part of one of the most fantastic chapters in American history.

Reynolds was the chief protagonist of the theory of a hollow earth, the inside of which was habitable. He lectured on this theme all over America and convinced thousands of converts; approximately twenty bills were introduced in Congress proposing that a Navy expedition sail into the globe's interior. Among Reynolds' converts was Edgar Allan Poe. The idea appears in several of his stories, and when the poet was dying of delirium tremens in a Baltimore hospital he called repeatedly for his friend.

On the way back up the western coast of South America the *Annawan* put in at Robinson Crusoe's island, Juan Fernandez, for provisions and repairs. There the ship was captured and held by Chilean convicts. At the last moment Palmer was rescued from a firing squad, according to a diary, now in the Library of Congress, of the ship's first mate, George Hubbard.

The experience seems to have soured the sea captain on anything connected with Antarctic exploration. He became a builder and captain of fast clipper ships engaged in the China trade, and in his later years was one of the chief owners of the New York–Fall River steamship line, best known as the subject of a somewhat ribald popular song.

Only within the past few years has Palmer's standing as an explorer been recognized, even in his own country. He made little effort to press his claims—probably he did not realize the significance of the discoveries. When he was a rich old gentleman, retired to his home in Stonington, "Captain Nat" used to hold his little niece on his knee and spin yarns of his boyhood adventures in the white darkness.

Palmer's claims rest on widely scattered, but seemingly reliable, evidence which has been assembled by Professor Hobbs. These claims have never been entirely recognized by British geographers; the northern peninsula of Antarctica usually is designated on British maps as Graham Land. This name was given the peninsula by Captain John Biscoe, commander of an expedition sent out by Enderby Brothers, a London whaling firm. Biscoe made a landfall there eleven years after Palmer's discovery; James Graham was Secretary of the Admiralty at the time. For many years it was argued that Palmer Land was not actually a part of the Antarctic Continent, but a large outlying island. There still remains some question, but in general geographers now agree that it is continuous with the major land mass.

Nathaniel Palmer died at his home in Stonington at the ripe old age of seventy-eight. He appears never to have made a systematic effort to arrange the logs and diaries he kept on his early voyages. Perhaps the rich shipping magnate was a little ashamed of his boyish enthusiasms for islands beyond the white rainbows of the southern ocean.

More than a million square miles of the Antarctic Continent now bear the name of Wilkes Land. They are named for truculent, obstinate Lieutenant Charles Wilkes, commander of five Navy ships which left the United States in 1838 for exploration of the Pacific and the Antarctic, with orders to reach the southernmost point possible.

The exploring fleet sailed south from Sydney the day after Christmas, 1839, and assembled near the Balleny Islands. Wilkes then proceeded westward through drifting ice for approximately a thousand miles. His course was nearly along the Antarctic Circle; most of the time his tempest-tossed ships were buried in fog and snow. On January 16, 1840, Lieutenant Ringgold, commander of the *Porpoise,* reported sighting land to the south, "like distant mountains." Three days later, at approximately 157.46 east longitude, sight of land was reported by three of the ships. On the last day of the month Wilkes wrote: "Land in sight and open water seen. We approached within half a mile of dark, volcanic rocks which appeared on both sides of us and saw land gradually rising beyond the ice to the height of some three thousand feet, and entirely covered with snow."

This was slightly east of the present Adélie coast. During the next two weeks, as the fleet continued westward, there were several reports of land, and on February 12 Wilkes reported sighting "from eighteen to twenty miles distant a lofty mountain range covered with snow."

No attempt was made to get a landing party ashore; rations were running short, and scurvy had made its appearance. The crews were mutinous; the obstinate and quarrelsome Wilkes was at odds with most of his officers.

He had no alternative but to leave the Antarctic, since the south polar winter was close at hand and new ice was forming.

For seventy-five years following the expedition's return many doubts were thrown on the validity of Wilkes' claims, for later exploring parties found no coast in the places reported. However, it now generally is admitted that Wilkes and his commanders were the first men ever to set eyes on the mainland of the Antarctic Continent of which the Palmer Peninsula, discovered two decades before, is a northward extension. Their landfalls came only in brief intervals of clear weather—they undoubtedly were victims of the phenomenon of "looming" which made the hills they saw appear as much as fifty miles closer than their actual position. It would have been difficult for five ships to have followed Wilkes' course without an occasional glimpse of coastline and, with due allowance for mirage, some of the positions given check fairly closely with the actual shore. So the name of the expedition's commander remains on most of the vast area of the plateau which lies back of the coast reported by him.

The United States has never considered these discoveries a basis for territorial claim; after the expedition's return, the country even seemed to lose interest. In the same seas at the time of Wilkes' findings was a French exploring party with two ships, the *Astrolabe* and the *Zelée*, under the command of Captain Dumont d'Urville. On January 20 this explorer sighted land about a hundred miles west of the first position reported by Wilkes four days before. A landing party went ashore on a small, rock-covered island near the ice cliff and planted the French tricolor, thus formally assuming possession of the region. Wilkes had named this same area after his wife, Adélie. France has claimed sovereignty ever since over the coastline extending approximately 135 miles between the 142nd and 137th east meridians and the territory extending inland to the South Pole.

The next year a British expedition under Sir James Clark Ross, whose sole objective was Antarctic exploration, entered the present Ross Sea and discovered the great ice shelf and the lofty mountain ranges of the western shore. Then interest in the Antarctic subsided for a half-century; it was not until fifty years later that any human being actually stepped foot on the continent. On January 23, 1894, Carstens E. Borchgrevink, a young Norwegian resident in Australia who had joined the crew of a Norse whaler for this specific purpose, went ashore at Cape Adare, the extreme northwestern edge of the Ross Sea. Four years later he returned in command of a privately financed British expedition and passed a six-months-long winter night in the same region.

For more than a century this coast remained a phantom. Large segments appeared, vanished, and reappeared in the reports of explorers. Ships sailed over areas where maps, drawn according to positions given by earlier expeditions, showed mountains. The first attempt at valid charting of the entire coastline of Wilkes Land was made by the western task force of the U. S. Navy's 1946–47 expedition under the command of Captain Charles Bond.

The findings were, for the most part, disappointing to the crews of the flying boats that Captain Bond was able to send out on the rare days of favorable weather. Their flights over the high ice cliffs with occasional protrusions of black rocks revealed little but flat, featureless ice everywhere; the occasional elevations seemed hardly more than hills. But actually these flyers were making one of the major geographic contributions of the expedition, though they themselves could not see vastness for emptiness. The absence of high mountains lining the coast and the monotonous ascent of the ice plain to elevations of more than seven thousand feet within 150 miles of the sea were discoveries of the first order of importance. Here was a thousand-mile break in the mountain ranges which rim most of the Antarctic Continent and the greatest extension of the titanic ice plain in the sky.

Land of Ghosts

The true picture of the Antarctic Continent has taken shape slowly during the century following these early voyages. It is a picture composed of such fabulous elements that they often outweigh the fancy of the pre-explorer imagination, for in the land at the bottom of the earth are encountered phenomena of nature so far outside ordinary experience as to suggest supernatural manifestations. They are eerie and beautiful and terrible, and science still gropes for understanding of many of these mysteries.

In the Antarctic the sky frequently is green when the sun is low on the horizon. The greenness, which is like that of a lawn in early spring, extends from the horizon halfway to the zenith; the closest analogy would be to a vivid green sunset. An extraordinary example of this was observed from the deck of the Coast Guard icebreaker *Northwind,* pushing southward through the ice pack on New Year's Eve, 1946. On the southern horizon appeared a green shore; close-mown lawns, bordered by hedges, sloped gently upward into eiderdown clouds. The effect was like a Chinese landscape painting, fifty miles long and ten miles high, suspended over the horizon.

No physical explanation of this is entirely satisfactory, but the phenomenon is believed caused in part by the reflection of white light from the sun at a different wavelength—it may be an "earthset," instead of a sunset, seen from the earth itself. Another factor may be the effect on white light of vast numbers of snow crystals in the atmosphere.

The late Dr. William J. Humphreys of the U. S. Weather Bureau has described green moons and green suns seen in middle latitudes, but he explains these as caused by very thick clouds of dust in the air. This explanation of course could not hold for the Antarctic, where dust does not exist. Again, meteorologists long have been puzzled by the "green flash" reported as a rare occurrence in the sub-Arctic. The flash, which usually appears in the sky just over the horizon shortly before sunset and lasts only a few seconds, is thought to be due to an electrical discharge from ice particles. It is possible that the green sky of the Antarctic is one of these green flashes lasting for a much longer period of time.

Of quite common occurrence in the Antarctic are halos around the sun and moon, caused by refraction and reflection through and from ice crystals. And strangest of all, men breathe rainbows. The moisture in the breath freezes instantly when it leaves the mouth, forming clouds of millions of floating ice crystals. Sunlight through these clouds creates a succession of rainbow-colored circles which appear to come from one's own lungs.

When a blizzard arose suddenly over the Antarctic one evening several winters ago, the drivers of two tractored jeeps became lost while attempting to make their way from the gasoline dump to the base camp—a distance of only two hundred yards. The drivers floundered helplessly in the dense whiteness where there were no landmarks and no shadows.

After about fifteen minutes the men remembered the instructions given them for such an emergency and were about to stop until the blizzard ended. Suddenly they found themselves back at the gasoline dump, in almost exactly the same spot from which they had started. Later examination of the tracks showed that they had made a complete circle, nearly a mile in radius, always turning left although both men insisted they had meant to bear to the right, in the direction of the camp.

This instinctive left-turning is a common phenomenon in Antarctica. Here everything which turns, naturally turns left. Lost men and dogs always circle to the left. Snow always swirls to the left. The sun in summer moves twenty-four hours a day around the high horizon, always from right to left. The remarkable fact is that even when men try consciously to turn right the sum of several turns is always to the left so that, without landmarks, it is almost impossible to avoid returning to one's starting point from the left.

The exact opposite is true in north polar regions where everything naturally turns right. There is an instinct, deeply rooted in the conscious, to turn right north of the equator and left south of the equator. The instinct appears to become more pronounced the farther north or south one goes; circles traversed by lost men sometimes reach extreme exactitude. The person who goes astray in the Antarctic and keeps on walking is almost certain to return to his starting point, if he lives long enough. Members of Rear Admiral Richard E. Byrd's expeditions recall instances where men tried deliberately to move with the wind, which was blowing in a right direction. In a short time they found themselves turned left and facing the wind, unable to understand how they had got themselves in this position. The instinct for downwind travel of course is very slight but the left-turning instinct is powerful.

This drive appears to be shared by all Antarctic animals. Penguin tracks in the snow always bear left; seals "swim" in left-turning circles over the névé; flocks of the voracious skuas which fly at a man as soon as he steps on the ice shelf seem always to approach from a leftward direction.

In some complex fashion the consciousness of man, bird, and seal is integrated with the whirling of a planet in space which in turn is integrated with the mechanics of solar system and galaxy. The lost jeep drivers returned to the gasoline dump because of the direction in which a mass of fiery gas torn loose from the sun was started rotating.

The left-turning mechanism in the brain is, of course, entirely subconscious. The men themselves had no more realization of it than of the fact that since crossing the Antarctic Circle each of them had gained almost a pound in weight—without putting on any extra flesh. This was due to the greater pull of gravity in the south polar region than in middle latitudes. Very close to the pole the pull is sufficient to cause a difference of about ten pounds per ton.

The weight of anything on the surface of the earth is measured by the gravitational pull of the earth itself which pulls everything toward the center balanced against the centrifugal force of the planet's rotation which tends to throw any loose object into space.

The distance to the earth's center is slightly less at either pole than at the equator. Hence, since the gravitational attraction between objects varies inversely with the square of their distance apart, the pull downward is greater by an infinitesimally minute amount. For an object weighing a ton it would be barely measurable with the most refined instruments. The balancing centrifugal force, however, disappears almost completely. The speed of the earth's rotation is about a thousand miles an hour at the equator; it is close to zero at either pole.

Weight also is increased slightly by the gravitational pull of such an enormous mass of ice and rock as the Antarctic Continent. It would be somewhat greater here than at the North Pole. Here the combination of factors meant an increase of nearly five hundred tons in the total weight of the Navy expedition and an increase of about a ton and a half in the combined weight of the four thousand men.

This unsensed weight increase has considerably more significance than a mere curiosity in the calculations of geophysics, for the figures become astronomical when applied to the polar icecap itself. Ice weighs about fifty pounds a cubic foot in middle latitudes. On this basis a minimum estimate of the total weight of the Antarctic ice would be about 10,000,000,000,000,000—that is, ten quadrillion—tons. The lessening of centrifugal force should increase this mass by two or three trillion tons. This is minute when compared with the total mass of the planet but there is a possibility that it has some bearing on the physics of the atmosphere in which small variations sometimes have far-reaching chains of effects. There is no such titanic ice mass in the Northern Hemisphere, which fact tends to make the planet very slightly "bottom heavy."

Awesome phenomena of Antarctica are the "flying seas," found in the windiest region in the world, Commonwealth Bay off the coast of Wilkes Land. Across this bay, about twenty-seven miles wide and twelve miles deep, an almost constant blizzard blows from the South Pole. Great whirlpools of snow on the continental plateau are raised to altitudes of as much as a thousand feet and blown northward at from fifty to ninety miles an hour. On the surface, though, it is calm; no snow falls. There is only the tumultuous snowstorm in the sky which accentuates the strange white darkness of a cloudy day.

This snow is precipitated over the sea and ice pack either as snow or rain. The Australian explorer, Sir Douglas Mawson, one of whose camps was established near Commonwealth Bay, estimated that in a year these swift-moving snow masses represent an area of water over the bay region about one and a quarter miles deep. In other words, an area of water one-fourth the size of Chesapeake Bay takes wings and flies.

Mawson and his men stayed at the bay all winter when the sea-carrying blizzards were at their worst. They found that wind velocities as high as a hundred miles an hour were not rare. Often the air traveled forward in a series of cyclonic gusts, with the greatest velocities at the centers.

For months at a time the drifting snows never ceased; many days passed, Mawson reported, when it was impossible to see one's hand at arm's length. It was a ghostly place in the bitter winter cold. The wind-blown snow became charged with electricity and in the perpetual darkness all pointed objects, such as one's nose and fingertips, glowed with the pale blue phantom light of St. Elmo's fire. All around, the white darkness was filled with these flitting blue will-o'-the-wisps.

The region is important because it may afford one of the best approaches to the South Pole for a land party. Beyond Commonwealth Bay the land appears to slope gently upward to the pole without the presence of mountain ranges such as the Queen Mauds which block off polar parties at the foot of the Ross Shelf. Here, however, an area of pack ice extends north from the continental shores almost to the circle, which has remained essentially unchanged for a hundred years.

Somewhat analogous to the flying-seas region are the "hell holes" found along the coast of the Bellingshausen Sea which was surveyed by planes of Admiral Byrd's 1939 expedition. Here great glaciers flow through high mountain passes and empty into bays which cut far into the land. The heavy, cold wind from the south polar plateau falls from the stratosphere over these glaciers and mixes with the warmer air from the seas. The result is nearly constant winds of from fifty to eighty miles an hour velocity which whip through the bays like exhaust from funnels. Mouths for such bays are almost impossible for navigation; twenty miles farther north, however, there may be dead calm.

Two of the most celebrated of these "hell holes" are

near Cape Colbeck at the foot of the Rockefeller Mountains and near Marguerite Bay on the eastern side of the Bellingshausen Sea. But similar exhaust valves of the enormous energies stored up over the continent are found all along the coast. The unbroken howling of the wind for days sometimes has driven men crazy.

A little farther to the east is the country of ice volcanoes. These strange formations in the shelf ice west of the Palmer Peninsula are gigantic bowls of ice, with floors as much as a mile in diameter surrounded by walls a hundred feet high; from above they look like miniatures of craters on the surface of the moon. Inside the bowls are little mountains of ice blocks thirty to forty feet high. The common explanation is that some sort of gas became entrapped in the shelf ice, resulting finally in an explosion with the formation of the craters; later explosions piled up the blocks inside them. Thus the phenomenon seems nearly to duplicate that of the volcano in solid ice, but on a much smaller scale.

Perhaps the most terrifying of Antarctic phenomena was reported by British explorers on one of the nearly motionless glaciers a few miles inland from the west coast of the Ross Sea. Over this glacier towers a lofty mountain. At almost the moment a shadow of the mountain falls on the ice on a sunny day there starts a succession of loud explosions, like mortar fire in battle. Sometimes the detonations last for a half-hour; it is as if a titanic photo-electric reaction had been set off by the shadow. Networks of tiny crevasses, some of them as much as a hundred feet long and ten inches deep, appear.

One of the curiosities of the southern seas is a poison

island. This is Zavodovski Island near South Georgia. From its numerous caves issue thin, reddish-brown clouds of sulphur-filled mist. Penguins, abundant on other islands near by, stay strictly away from this volcanic ice-covered rock. All efforts to land have been defeated by the poisonous fumes, which were as bad as ever when Frank Wild, who succeeded Sir Ernest Shackleton in command of his last expedition after the leader's death at sea, passed near the place in 1921.

The weirdest of all Antarctic phenomena are associated with light and some of them are at present inexplicable—such as sudden veils of blueness that fall over the world and vanish in a few minutes. A venerable gentleman now living in Washington, Dr. Henryk Arctowski, one evening in 1898 stood on the deck of the exploring ship *Belgica* which was entirely surrounded by pack ice in the Bellingshausen Sea somewhere west of the Palmer Peninsula. He was the physicist of the Belgian expedition of which Roald Amundsen, future discoverer of the South Pole, and Dr. Frederick A. Cook, later discredited claimant to the discovery of the North Pole, were members, and which drifted for more than a year in the Bellingshausen pack.

"At a given moment," says Dr. Arctowski, "the ice suddenly assumed an intense blue color of extraordinary purity, a little tinged with purple near the horizon. Fog and ice were colored alike, hence they must have been illuminated with blue light. It was clear enough to see floating ice a mile away."

Officers on watch on the deck of the Navy's flagship *Mount Olympus* early one morning while she was anchored in the Bay of Whales observed for about four hours a hitherto unrecorded optical phenomenon—the sudden appearance of an enormous ink-black patch in a clear blue sky. The ship's radar had just detected a gigantic iceberg somewhere outside the bay about four miles away. A sharp watch was ordered but the monster remained invisible. Then, over the approximate position indicated by the radar for the berg, appeared a single black spot. It bore no resemblance to a cloud. A few minutes later five similar black spots appeared extended in a straight line many miles to the north. All slowly changed shape during the four hours, after which they faded away almost as suddenly as they had appeared. The top of the iceberg was glimpsed only after the phenomenon had been in progress for two hours. A probable explanation for the first inkspot was the mirroring of this floating ice mountain in the sky directly above it, but the other spots were unexplainable, unless caused by smaller icebergs not located by the radar.

Quite frequently white rainbows were seen from the ship's deck above the bay ice. These appeared as broad, milk-white bands in a solid blue sky; they are similar to ordinary rainbows and are caused by refraction of light by water droplets in fog. The smaller the droplets, the lighter the colors, with more refractions from the violet end of the solar spectrum where radiation becomes invisible. Finally the blueness fades entirely, leaving only shimmering bands of whiteness.

White Darkness

Antarctica is the land of white darkness.

Day after day the landscape is veiled in a thick, downy whiteness in which visibility is at times non-existent. Strange things happen, such as the sudden disappearance before the eyes of moving objects.

Two men, dressed in white, may be walking across the snow side by side. They are in a world of complete whiteness. The air is white; earth and sky are white; the wind in the face is white with clouds of snow. Suddenly one man becomes conscious that the other no longer is walking beside him. He has disappeared, as though the thin, white air has dissolved him. Yet he continues to talk as if nothing has happened, unaware that he has become a substanceless phantom. His voice is unchanged; it seems to come from the same direction and the same distance. A moment later he reappears—perhaps floating in the air a few feet ahead and at about eye-level. Still he talks as if he were walking beside the other man. He has no awareness of his own preternatural levitation.

There is no satisfactory physical or psychological explanation of this bewildering phenomenon. Dr. Paul Siple, chief scientist of the Navy expedition, has formulated a theory, admittedly without complete substantiating data, exploring a major part of the observed happenings. These vanishings occur only on "white days," when the sky is overcast with white clouds—which results, Siple believes, in the physical phenomenon of multiple reflection. Multiple reflection is essentially unknown to physicists because it occurs only in the Antarctic—possibly in the Arctic on a smaller scale—and is unduplicable in any laboratory. Its major effect is the accumulation of imprisoned light between earth and sky like the accumulation of heat in a greenhouse: vision becomes drowned in light.

The surface of earth and sea is almost completely white; it cannot absorb light or heat and reflects practically all the visible and invisible radiation from the sun. So far as heat radiation is concerned, a striking confirmation of Dr. Siple's theory was found by Navy scientists in the Antarctic. The temperature of the peculiarly sandlike snow was taken daily to a depth of one inch and was found consistently to be about 5 degrees lower than that of the air immediately above the surface. This supposedly was due to the immediate re-radiation upward of all heat received from the sun and its very rapid dissipation.

With light, however, the problem is more difficult and not so susceptible to experimentation. When the sky is clear all reflected visible light and ultraviolet radiation presumably pass through it almost instantaneously and are lost in space. The white landscape is lit only by the light coming from the sun at any particular instant. But what happens when thick white clouds, whose reflecting power nearly equals that of the snow itself, completely cover the heavens? Presumably a large part of the reflected light hits an impassable barrier—it is unable to escape and is reflected back to earth again. Then once more it is bounced back against the impenetrable wall of the cloud-covered sky. Reflection and re-reflection continue at the rate of many thousand times a second—180,000 if the clouds happen to be a mile high. At a certain instant x amount of radiation hits the snow and is bounced back to the sky in 180,000th of a second. A great deal of it is unable to get through and comes back to earth again, added to the new radiation which at that instant is coming from the sun. The process continues indefinitely so long as the sky remains covered with white clouds.

This results in what Siple calls "the complete antithesis of darkness"—absolute whiteness, to which the human eye is little better adjusted than to darkness; in fact, vision in white darkness may be more difficult than in black darkness. Accompanying this visible light there is bound to be an enormous amount of the invisible, germ-killing ultraviolet that causes sunburn, which probably adds something to the brilliance of the white light. The presence of ultraviolet is proved by a striking phenomenon—in the Antarctic on a white day the most likely part of the body to become sunburned is the exposed bottom of the chin, or the palms of the hands if the weather is mild enough so that gloves are not required. Serious sunburn is likely to be a major problem on Antarctic expeditions, for there is no escape from this invisible ultraviolet radiation. It comes from all directions and at all angles. Tinted glasses, of course, are essential in the snowfields at any time; without them serious cases of snow blindness result in a very short time. But they are of little help to vision in white darkness.

Another apparent contradiction to the laws of physics first was experienced by Dr. Siple while engaged in a survey on the ice shelf about two miles south of the tent camp and at an elevation about fifty feet higher. The tents were easily visible across the snow and Siple, busy at his job, paid no particular attention to them. Then he became aware that they had enormously enlarged. The camp loomed before his eyes like a city of pyramidal skyscrapers. However startling, this was not too difficult to explain as a rather extraordinary example of "looming," the most common of the Antarctic mirages. What followed, however, belongs in the world of complete upsidedownness.

A cloud drifted across the sun and there was a slight change in the wind direction. In the twinkling of an eye the tents disappeared completely, and before the observer stretched an empty field of snow. Mystified, he dropped to his knees. The camp of brown skyscrapers immediately reappeared. When he arose it disappeared again. He repeated the performance several times, always with the same result. Dr. Siple probably is the only living man who has seen a greater distance across the surface of the earth by looking up than by looking down.

In white darkness there are no shadows; these are seen only when the sun is high in a cloudless sky. As a result Antarctica most of the time is a shadowless land. On a cloudy day the illumination of the landscape is so diffuse that there is no perspective by which one can estimate the contours, size, or distance of white objects. The feet cannot find the snow underfoot. One staggers and stumbles like a drunken man. Walking becomes extremely difficult and tiresome. Sledge and tractor drivers cannot move for days at a time until shadows reappear by which they can detect the parallel ridges which indicate the presence of crevasses. Otherwise they might well stumble blindfolded into an area crisscrossed with thousand-foot-deep rifts in the ice which are the death traps of polar explorers.

Elsewhere, perhaps, shadows do not play an important part in life. But in the infinity of whiteness black images on the snow provide a pattern by which the human mind can function. Without them the difficulties of finding one's way are enormously multiplied. They may mean the difference between reason and utter confusion—in extreme cases between life and death. Where all reality is white it vanishes in whiteness, and the world is left empty of substance.

Beyond Time

Man's mind is conscious of time through the recurrence of events, the succession of day and night, the parade of seasons, the rising and falling of tides, the progression of growing old. Only within one's own body and in the changing constellations of the winter skies in the Antarctic is any change discernible except undifferentiated duration. The processes of rot, rust, fermentation, mould, disease either are absent altogether, or proceed so slowly that there is no consciousness of them. About the only natural clock is the erosion activated by the creeping of groaning glaciers, the wearing down of mountains by inches in centuries.

Antarctica knows no dying. This is literally true, because beyond the mountain rim nothing dies of its own physiological processes. Here is the reality of the dream of a land of perpetual youth, but a mockery for man because the price for not growing old is unliving. It is aging in death, rather than aging in life, which is suspended.

The Antarctic Continent has been in a state of suspended

animation for several thousands of millenniums. It is not
entirely beyond possibility, however fantastic, that if the
icecap were suddenly disintegrated—say by the dropping
of a few thousand plutonium bombs to produce a habitable
continent—the one-celled spores of the vegetation of a
hundred million years ago might germinate, and forests
of tree ferns and club mosses fill the glacial valleys. Also
ancient viruses, possibly even the more complex bacteria,
might come to life and descend upon the world.

Of more practical and immediate significance—Antarctica is the natural icebox of the world. If all the grain
produced on earth this year were dumped on the continent it would be as edible as ever a hundred years from
now. If all the cows, hogs, and sheep slaughtered in the
United States were consigned to the ice they would be
available to the great-great-great grandchildren of the
present generation. Once the materials were transported
the perfect refrigeration would be had at no cost whatsoever.

This might be a fact of very great social and economic
importance for the world. A major reason for the famines
which devastate large areas of the globe is crop failure.
The doomful Malthusian theory that human populations
always will tend to increase faster than the capacity of the
earth to feed them—whereupon they must be decimated
by the swords of the four horsemen—still holds true although not so obviously as when it was propounded a century and a half ago. Throughout its history mankind either
has had an abundance of food or a tragic scarcity, with
peaks and troughs recurring in unpredictable cycles. Only
within the past half-century has there been much success

in distributing good harvests over bad years by means of insect-proof and fungus-proof grain elevators, cold storage plants for meats, and dehydration processes for fruits, eggs, and vegetables. All these have been costly and of limited application.

On the Antarctic Continent the temperature almost never rises above the freezing point of water, and it is thought to sink as low as 100 degrees below zero. There are no bugs to eat grain, no bacteria to spoil meat, no spores to mould bread. Nearly all foodstuffs could be preserved at no expense whatever, except for transportation. At present, of course, this cost would be enormous although hardly comparable with that of an equal amount of refrigeration obtained in any other way.

The idea has brewed for some years in the mind of Admiral Byrd, who has suggested that Antarctica be placed under world trusteeship as an insurance against recurrent food shortages. At present the continent could serve best as a storehouse of the enormous food surpluses of the Southern Hemisphere—Argentine wheat and beef, Australian mutton, New Zealand cheese and butter. There is every prospect that with rapidly increasing populations in the Northern Hemisphere the relatively sparsely populated southern continents will be called upon more and more to feed the world. Both physically and politically, Antarctica is much more suitable as a world refrigerator than any place near the North Pole, such as the middle of Greenland. There the cold is far less stable and the thermometer sometimes rises above the freezing point for weeks at a time. Bacteria and mould spores are in the air; it would be necessary to protect stores from bears and foxes. Of even greater importance, the Arctic basin may lie in the path of invading armies in any future war. Antarctica, on the other hand, is far removed physically from the world's squabbles; the icecap will never become a battlefield, unless for the specific object of capturing supplies stored there.

Several experiences of the 1947 Navy expedition illustrated the potentialities of this ageless land. One such was the helicopter descent of Rear Admiral Richard H. Cruzen on the camp at Cape Evans, near McMurdo Sound, which had been abandoned by Captain Robert F. Scott more than thirty-five years before. From the camp's appearance, the occupants might have left only within the past few days. Boards and rafters of the cabin looked as if they had just come from the sawmill; there was no rot in the timbers, not a speck of rust on the nailheads. A hitching rope used for Manchurian ponies looked new and proved as strong as ever when it was used to hitch the helicopter. Biscuits and canned meat still were edible, although they seemed to have lost a little of their flavor. A sledge dog, which apparently had frozen to death while standing up, still stood there looking as if it were alive. A London magazine, published in Scott's day and exposed to the elements since his departure, might have been printed that morning.

This suggests the possibility of establishing on the Antarctic Continent a world library for the storage of everything that comes off the printing presses. It would be safe from all the agencies that age and destroy books and papers; the cheapest newsprint would be as good, and the type on it just as readable, in five hundred years.

Parties from the Navy expedition visited two of the previous Little America camps, buried for seven and fourteen years beneath six to ten feet of hardpacked névé. At the second station the visitors ate raisin cookies, butter, and candy—all as good as ever. In the messes of the *Mount Olympus,* more than two hundred pounds of six-year-old butter was served; from a side of beef seven years old, juicy steaks were cut. Both seemed to have improved with time.

At the other camp, which had been abandoned fourteen years before, Admiral Byrd came upon a strange phenomenon—that of baking with cold instead of with heat. Among the stores which the Admiral had left when he abandoned camp was a crate of apples; they were frozen hard but when thawed had about the taste, texture, and juiciness of apples baked in an oven. For fourteen years they had been in a constant temperature between 5 and 10 degrees below zero, the year-round average for this part of Antarctica. This temperature fluctuates very little, summer and winter, below the ice. Candy also seemed undeteriorated. Bread and meat were as good as ever. Oranges seemed rather tasteless and butter a trifle rancid, but the deterioration processes might have been underway before they were put in storage. The possibilities of cold baking remain to be determined by experiment but there is reason to believe that it would be successful with most fruits and vegetables —that potatoes, for example, could be as well baked by cold as by heat.

Wherever Antarctic explorers go, extra food is cached for the benefit of others who may follow them. One of the trail parties of the last Byrd expedition dined well on supplies left in this way by Amundsen nearly thirty years before, and in 1945 the British Falkland Islands Dependencies Survey party visited Seymour Island, east of the Palmer Peninsula. Says their report: "The sledging party visited a food depot left by Nordenskjöld [Swedish Antarctic explorer] and dined well on forty-five-year-old corned beef, canned beans, and sugar. They also visited Nordenskjöld's camp and Snow Island. Window panes were broken and some of the rooms filled with snow but otherwise everything was in good order. A magazine, unread for forty years, seemed as fresh as ever."

Another curious fact observed was that in Antarctica no garbage pails, garbage disposal plants, or sewage systems are necessary. All that is required is a hole in the ice. Overnight each day's garbage sinks a foot or so. It is only necessary to dump the next day's waste on top of it. This could be continued every day for years, until the accumulation reached the bottom of the ice.

The practical possibility of using Antarctica as a world icebox will remain quite speculative until more is known of the long-time effects of cold; at present the chemistry and physiology of cold are little-explored fields of science. Within the past decade has been announced the sensational finding that various low organisms—among them probably various disease germs—may be placed in states of suspended animation for long periods by quick freezing in which water is transformed from liquid to glass without passing through a phase of ice crystallization which rips the envelopes of living cells and thus destroys them.

With improved transportation facilities this land on the edge of time may have considerable potentialities as a health resort. Here is earth's richest, dryest, purest air. Dust particles, pollen grains, fungus spores, and bacteria exist only in such minute quantities as to be negligible. Complete insurance is provided against the common allergies such as ragweed, colds, and rose fever. The wind always blows northward from the sterile South Pole. Were it not for the extreme cold, which in winter can sear lungs like blue-hot flame, this high, dry land, whose air is sterilized by enormous amounts of ultraviolet radiated from every direction twenty-four hours a day during the three months of summer, might be an ideal location for tuberculosis sanatoria.

The experience of the Navy expedition was typical. Colds and influenza disappeared among the crews, and sick bays emptied about two weeks out of Panama. After that none appeared until late January when the airplane crews arrived at Little America, bringing a supply of germs, when a mild epidemic broke out which lasted for about a week. Following this there were no more colds until a few days after the ships docked at New Zealand.

There is only one contagious disease native to the Antarctic—"speck finger," which is sometimes contracted while cutting up seal meat. It is characterized by indolent abscesses on the sites of small cuts or scratches. Some cases have been so serious as to require finger amputation, and extreme care in handling dead seals always is necessary.

Another Antarctic malady is "cabin fever," which is found also in the Far North. It is manifested not by increase in body temperature but by extreme irritability. This, however, is not transmissible by any physical agent. Its probable cause is given by Dr. Russell G. Frazier, medical officer of the 1939 Byrd expedition:

An increased amount of adrenalin in the blood stream was observed while giving local anaesthetics for tooth extractions. At first eight minims were used to an ounce of novocaine solution. This resulted in an adrenalin shock to the patient. The same solution was administered to a second patient with a similar result. The third patient received only four minims to the ounce, which likewise produced an adrenalin shock. On the fourth patient two minims were used, and still a slight reaction was noted.

This increase of adrenalin owing to the cold is a very vital factor in cold acclimatization. It contracts the arteries and capillaries, thereby speeding up the blood flow through the exposed skin. It sends the blood back into the deeper organs to be warmed, and it mobilizes liver glycogen to meet an immediate demand for additional heat. It stimulates cellular metabolism and by the contraction of the small terminal vessels causes the skin and subcutaneous tissues to lose a great percent of their water. It increases blood pressure and slows the heart and respiratory rate directly through the autonomic nervous system. A great deal of the touchiness of individuals during the long, cold winter night is believed due to this increased adrenalin secretion and "cabin fever" may be attributed to the same condition.

Seals, penguins, and men die in Antarctica—but not, so far as is known, from infectious or contagious diseases. How adult penguins die, other than as victims of sea leopards and killer whales, nobody knows. The purely physical perils that beset life are great; most of the man-aping birds probably do not survive long enough to succumb to old age. They appear to have not the slightest resistance to any disease organism which they meet in the outside world.

The first human child has yet to be born below the Antarctic Circle. One who first saw the light there might pass an entire lifetime in a completely sterilized, aseptic world. The child would never contract colds, mumps, measles, chickenpox, grippe, unless some visitor introduced the germs. Then, having acquired no resistance, it probably would die of the first minor illness to come along.

Whales in the Sky

In the Antarctic the sun may rise in the west and set in the east. There are double and triple sunrises and sunsets. There are mornings in the evening and evenings in the morning.

Ships sail upside-down in the clouds. In the middle of the ice shelf one may see vessels, smoke pouring from their funnels, floating among icebergs a few miles away although actually no open water is within a hundred miles. Wild mountain landscapes, grossly distorted, loom on the skyline. They look as though they could be reached easily in a few hours, but in reality they are weeks away. These phantoms are the scenery which lies beyond the horizon; all the Antarctic is a great hall of mirrors in the sky.

In 1912 the survivors of Scott's party waited anxiously for weeks at their McMurdo Sound camp for the return from New Zealand of their ship, the *Terra Nova*, which was to take them back to civilization. They had no assurance that it would be able to negotiate the pack in time to save them from another terrible winter. Day after day they scanned the northern horizon with their field glasses. H. G. Ponting, the expedition photographer, relates:

About noon on January 17 I was sweeping the north with the glasses when suddenly the masts of a ship came into the field of view. For a moment I could scarcely believe my eyes, but there could be no doubt about it. They were the masts of a barque, but presenting an extraordinary appearance for they towered unnaturally high above the skyline. Then I saw that what I was looking at was but a mirage. The real ship was hull-down below the horizon and only the masts were visible. Above them a wonderful mirage of the entire vessel, hull and all, appeared inverted. And over this first reflection there was a second mirage of the ship upright. It was this upper image I had seen first. The *Terra Nova* was about thirty miles away.

Probably unprecedented was a mirage seen by several members of Sir Ernest Shackleton's party in 1914. The incident is described in Shackleton's diary:

Walsy was in the crow's nest watching for signs of land to the westward and he reported an interesting phenomenon. The sun set amid a glow of prismatic colors on a line of clouds just above the horizon. A moment later he saw a golden glow which expanded as he watched it, and presently the sun appeared again and rose a semi-diameter clear above the western horizon. He hailed C———, who from a position on the floe ninety feet below the crow's nest also saw the reborn sun. A quarter of an hour later from the deck Walsy saw the sun set a second time. We attributed this strange phenomenon to an ice crack to the westward where the band of open water had heated strata of air.

Even more remarkable was the phenomenon of false sunrises and false sunsets reported by Shackleton:

The sun had set and gone away altogether. I had taken the sun for the last time and said we would not see it again for ninety days. Then after eight days it got up again. It had gone away and risen by refraction. On other days we watched the sun set all right, and come up again, and set about five times until we got tired of it.

Such a false sunrise was witnessed also by the officers on watch on the Navy flagship *Mount Olympus* a few mornings after Christmas. Following a few moments of twilight, the sun was seen rising in the west; the eastern horizon was hidden in banked clouds. The ship sailed for about two hours through a wide, straight avenue of clear atmosphere bounded north and south by great fog banks. Suddenly, within a period of minutes, the fog cleared and the northern heavens were streaked from zenith to horizon with four vertical rainbows, like enormous ribbons hanging from the top of the sky. A few moments later a double horizontal rainbow was reported.

These illusions are complex optical phenomena arising

from the banding of light as it passes through atmospheric layers of different temperatures and densities. About a half-mile above sea level the temperature of the air abruptly becomes about 10 degrees warmer; this is known as an "inversion layer." The stratum of warm air acts as a titanic mirror of scenes beyond the horizon.

Mirages of palm-shaded oases have beckoned thirst-crazed Sahara travelers to their doom. The word "mirage" first came into literature when Napoleon's soldiers in Egypt were startled by the appearance of phantom blue lakes in the hot sands. Such mirages are common to polar regions and deserts, but in the ice fields they are encountered on a far grander scale than in the sand oceans. They have been responsible for many misunderstandings between explorers. The American commander Wilkes, for example, described a coastline of towering mountains west of the Ross Sea. He gave precise longitudes and latitudes. Nearly seventy-five years later, when Captain Scott sailed across the site of these mountains, his soundings showed a thousand fathoms of water. Wilkes had been a victim of "looming." The sight he described probably lay far beyond his horizon—he was looking around the curvature of the earth. Yet for a century the incident cast doubt on all his claims to Antarctic discoveries.

Admiral Robert E. Peary was the victim of a similar hallucination in the Arctic. It was not until nearly twenty-five years later that his "Crocker Land" north of Ellesmere Island—reported in 1906 and thought by some to be a land mass of continental proportions—was proved a myth. But nobody ever questioned that Peary was an honest and accurate reporter.

The mirage is an extremely complex physical phenomenon which can be described with complete accuracy only in mathematical language. The explanation accepted by the Navy is that of the eminent American geographer, Professor William H. Hobbs of the University of Michigan. Professor Hobbs writes:

The peculiarly characteristic polar, or superior, mirage is strongly contrasted in nature with the much better known desert type, or inferior mirage. The latter is due to layers of hotter air which lie close to the desert surface with the hottest layer next to the surface, a highly unstable condition and hence seen usually only with conditions of quiet air. On our modern surfaced highways this phenomenon is nearly always to be seen on cold but sunny days, and quiet days when one comes up a grade to a flat section of the highway, the effect being the mirrored sky as seen in a pool of water.

This phenomenon, also fairly characteristic of the polar areas, is one of relatively short distances, usually measured in rods, whereas the looming of the high latitudes is not one of rods or even miles, but of tens or hundreds of miles. The deviation of the light rays from the object to the eye in the case of inferior mirage is always in a curve that is convex downward toward the earth's surface, whereas with superior mirage it is by contrast concave downward. With the rays bent convexly toward the earth as in desert mirage, the height of the eye sets the very low limit to the distance of objects seen as a consequence of it, and the image is an inverted one, usually of the sky, although sometimes of rocks and trees.

Superior mirage is due to a stratum of warmer layers of air above colder ones at some considerable distance above the surface—inversion of a temperature gradient so that the layers within the stratum are warmer upward. Studies made with ballons-sondes which carry self-recording instruments have shown that the inversions which are most characteristic of the polar regions, and particularly within the areas about the great continental glaciers, generally begin either at a height of a thousand to fifteen hundred meters, or else in the neighborhood of two hundred meters.

Because of the high altitude of the inversion layer the object seen must be at a very considerable distance, if the observer is near sea level and the object is beyond the normal horizon. Moreover, since the range of temperature difference within the inversion layer is limited to a few degrees centigrade in a vertical distance of five hundred meters or more, the refraction curve of the ray must be one of very long radius of curvature—that is, the curve must be very flat. It is a further peculiarity of the real image that enters the eye that it is expanded vertically so that objects are considerably distorted when seen by superior mirage. It follows from both these conditions that the object can be seen only from within a very limited area—the segment of a ring. Obviously at points nearer the object the curvature of the rays would not be sufficient to bring them down to earth.

It is characteristic of the high superior mirage that above one thousand meters there is usually a band which separates the raised image from the true horizon. In the case of the lower type, that near two hundred meters, it may be the top of the object which is truncated in the image.

The not uncommon phenomenon of superior mirage has been responsible for many false estimates of the remoteness of newly discovered land features which have been seen by explorers within the polar regions, combined as it has been with the underestimates due to the unusual clarity of the atmosphere. In many cases of snow-covered lands there is not enough of individual character in the coastal features to permit identification from different ship positions, and in such cases the newly discovered lands have of necessity been placed upon the maps on the basis of their direction and estimated distance. As a consequence, they are often from forty to fifty geographical miles too near when this is due to atmospheric clarity alone, and as much as two to three hundred miles when due to high superior mirage. In this way many of the puzzling confusions have arisen and explorers have repeatedly and quite unjustly been brought into discredit by later ship captains, who have arrived off these shores when sea-ice conditions were more favorable and have permitted nearer approach, or when atmospheric conditions were less deceptive. To errors in latitude were, in the case of earlier explorers, added the considerable uncertainty of longitude determination which, before the advent of radio time signals, were often in error by two or more degrees, even after checking the chronometer.

However deceptive, the Antarctic mirage is likely to prove a good friend to the explorer for it enables him to see land and ice fields far beyond the normal range of vision. He knows that the scenery which appears in the sky looking-glass in front of him is not a fantasy of the imagination. It actually exists somewhere, usually less than fifty miles away, and in the same general direction in which it appears. Not infrequently the picture is sufficiently accurate to be checked against maps and descriptions of the area.

A peculiar type of mirage, the so-called "fata morgana," is quite frequent in the ice pack. It is due to warm air layers over open water pools. Slight irregularities in the ice, probably only a few feet high, appear in the distance like majestic white towers and church steeples piercing the sky. This phenomenon is most likely when the sun is low in the sky around midnight. The "fata morgana" also is encountered in middle latitudes and has given rise to many superstitions; a familiar case is the so-called "Spectre of the Brocken," viewed from the highest point in the Harz Mountains. The observer sees an enormously magnified shadow of himself cast upon a bank of clouds when the sun is low in the high mountains. It is a gigantic, misty image which reproduces every movement of the man.

Mirages ordinarily are seen intermittently but during a tractor trek from Little America to the Rockefeller Mountains in the winter of 1947 the veteran Antarctic explorer, Captain Vernon D. Boyd of the U. S. Marine Corps, reported a continuous panorama of these mirrored images for more than twelve hours. Great broken walls of icebergs loomed ahead. Sometimes they would merge into a solid blue wall which, it seemed, formed an impenetrable barrier to any further progress. Throughout the day it appeared that the party was rapidly approaching an iceberg-filled sea—yet the nearest open water was Okuma Bay, which cuts into the Ross Shelf about sixty miles north of the line of march. The wall which confronted Boyd and his men was a blue phantom—a distorted image of this berg-filled inlet.

The Antarctic night lasts more than two thousand hours —the ninety days of the northern summer. It is a haunted night of bitter cold and screeching blizzards, broken by long interludes when moonlight and starlight over blue ice mountains and the endless white cemetery of pack and shelf produce an atmosphere unduplicable in creation. The completely translucent air and the glittering reflections from the crystals of the névé give one the illusion of being a disembodied spirit stranded in the great emptiness of space. The stars shine from the skies above, the snow underfoot, and the mountains round about.

Then the skies are hung with ethereal, fluttering, green curtains: these are the southern lights, the aurora australis. They are a duplicate of the northern lights and due to the same causes, but differ in some significant ways, especially in the quite irregular distribution and the soap-bubble tenuousness. The curtains are so thin that the moon and stars shine through them.

Whales in the Sky

"It is the language of mystic signs and portents," wrote Captain Scott in his diary. "The eastern sky was massed with swaying auroral light. Fold on fold, the arches and curtains of vibrating luminosity rose and spread across the sky. The brighter light seemed to flow, now to mass itself in wreathing folds in one quarter from which lustrous streamers shot upward, and now to run in waves. The appeal is to the imagination by the suggestion of something wholly spiritual, something instinct with fluttering ethereal life. One wonders why history does not tell us of aurora worshipers."

The aurora australis is so evanescent that it is extremely difficult to photograph, or even to describe its color with any assurance. Around the Bay of Whales it is predominantly white with zephyrs of green and rose wafted across and through it. Around McMurdo Sound, base of several British expeditions, the characteristic color is described as "pale straw yellow." There it often appeared first against the sky in gaps between the mountains. Fluttering waves would rise one after the other until they formed an apparently windblown curtain suspended from the zenith, sometimes culminating in a corona of folding light around the sky.

Physicists have not entirely succeeded in explaining this transcendent phenomenon, but the most generally accepted analysis is that the polar lights are caused by streams of electrically charged particles shot from the flaming surface of the sun at a velocity a little less than that of light. These particles are pulled toward the north and south magnetic poles of the earth. At an altitude of somewhere between sixty and two hundred miles they strike the extremely tenuous atmosphere and knock outer electrons from the shells of oxygen and nitrogen atoms. These thus are rendered briefly luminous. Their characteristic lines are found in auroral spectra, and the light itself can be reproduced in laboratory experiments. Presumably the levels of the atmosphere where this takes place are quite hot—somewhere near the boiling point of water. This has been the conclusion of meteorologists for some years on theoretical considerations, in the face of the common experience that the higher one goes the colder it gets. The hypothesis lately has been substantiated by rocket ascensions.

In the Northern Hemisphere the aurora borealis sometimes is seen quite deep in middle latitudes, usually at the time of great cyclones in the flaming atmosphere of the sun when extraordinarily large streams of particles are projected into space. In the Southern Hemisphere the aurora australis never has been reported north of the Antarctic Circle. It is a paler, more ghostly phenomenon than its northern counterpart.

The distribution of these lights is curious. Somewhere in the center of Marie Byrd Land, east of the Ross Sea, is a mathematical point known as the aurora pole. The aurora seems to take place in an approximate circle within a radius of about two hundred miles around this pole. Thus the phenomenon is quite prominent over the Ross Sea region but seldom has been observed in the Palmer Peninsula or around the Weddell Sea. These areas lie outside the radius of the circle.

Several observers have reported that the southern lights "sing"—that during the most brilliant displays there is a swishing sound like that of a silk dress. Some say the noise swells and fades as the aurora increases and diminishes in intensity. The sound hardly springs from the lights themselves—they are too distant. During a display, however, the atmosphere is intensely electrified and the phenomenon may be caused by brush discharges close to the ground.

The most extended study of the southern lights was carried out during Admiral Byrd's 1941 expedition. For the first time it was possible to obtain good photographs of the displays and to differentiate the different types. Captain Murray A. Weiner, in charge of the observation program, recorded some curious forms. One is a green flush close to the horizon, like an early dawn. There are pulsating lights which appear and disappear rhythmically several times in the same spot within a few seconds. There are the well-known rustling curtains which unmistakably resemble greenish-white draperies hung over the whole sky. Most striking of all are the "flaming aurora," strong waves of green and rose light moving across the sky with the appearance of a rapidly spreading green fire.

Two golden crosses float high among the southern stars through the winter night. One is the true cross, the other the false cross. The first is a small golden configuration of four stars like a crucifix on a wall, difficult to detect among the welter of constellations. It stands almost directly over the South Pole and through the centuries, since the first whalers entered these angry waters, it has been the unfailing guide of mariners.

Just below it, and about eight times its size, is the celestial false cross set like an ignis fatuus in the skies by the malevolent spirits of the south. It moves in an ellipse of

wide radius around the pole and has led many ships off
their courses in the night. A curious phenomenon was observed during the brief hour of darkness on Christmas Eve
as ships of the central Navy group entered the Antarctic:
A curiously shaped cloud drifted across the false cross, and
for a moment it looked as though a human figure were
nailed to the star arms.

Far in the south, almost over the pole, are clearly de-
fined the two Clouds of Magellan, like strayed patches of
the Milky Way. They are the farthest objects the human
eye can see—immense aggregations of stars and systems of
stars whose light has traveled at a speed of about 180,000
miles a second for almost a million years across a starless
gulf of space.

When Winter Comes

On a still day when the water temperature falls to approximately 29 Fahrenheit, or about one-tenth of a degree below the normal freezing point of salt water, a white gossamer forms over the black, oily water of lanes and pools in the ice pack. This is made up of very thin ice crystals which first appear patterned in scattered little squares and circles. They soon join to constitute a lacy veil and in a few hours change into a sheet of thin ice.

This phenomenon of extraordinary beauty takes place in late February or early March, the beginning of the Antarctic autumn. It is preceded for several days by scattered pillars of gray smoke, like the smoke of burning leaves during a northern autumn. This is "frost smoke," foglike clouds which rise from water surfaces on contact of the cold air with the warmer water below.

Frost smoke appears at about the time of the first brief interludes of dusk and then darkness that relieve the monotony of summer's twenty-four-hour-long days. These are nostalgic twilights for men who have grown weary of light. The rapidly succeeding sunrises and sunsets at first are only rosy flashes on the green horizons, but the intervals between them grow longer very rapidly until finally there are only stars and a moon in the sky. Under their dim light the snow fields sparkle as if scattered with diamonds.

Men have seldom had a better opportunity to watch this spectacle than the crew of the icebreaker *Northwind,* on a reconnaissance run through the floe ice in late February, 1947. From the deck it was possible to watch the pattern taking shape from minute to minute. For several days the salt water temperature had been barely at the freezing point and a fraction of a degree drop was sufficient to start the strange lace weaving. It usually is preceded by a few hours of unusual calm, and the oily appearance of the water is apparently also characteristic of the transition zone of temperature. When the *Northwind* crew observed it around Scott Island in December they became quite pessimistic over the depth of the pack likely to be encountered on the way to Little America.

Once the lace appears, consolidation of the pack into a solid unnavigable sheet is likely to proceed very rapidly if there is a quick drop of 10 or 15 degrees in temperature, a common occurrence in the Antarctic. Such a change may take place in a few moments. Once the thin ice film—it may be only a fraction of an inch thick—cements the fragments of the pack broken by the summer sun, a "flash" freeze may close all leads in a single night.

By far the greater part of the ice packs which belt the Antarctic Continent is the frozen surface of the sea, formed each autumn in much the way described above. But woven into the pattern are stranded icebergs, bergy bits, and great ribs of ice broken from the edge of the shelves which have drifted northward and become trapped in flash freezes. Only a few weeks before, the Navy expedition had watched the pack disintegrating, a gradual process extending over months beginning with the advent of summer in late October. The sea ice formed in the preceding winter —light, full of trapped air, alive with diatoms and from three to ten feet thick—softens from day to day under the sun's rays. Its snow blanket melts and fresh water ponds are formed. This disintegrating ice is soft and slushy and is easily cracked by wind and wave. Straight-banked rivers and jagged-shored lakes appear where the ice has cracked; the lakes resemble vast gardens of white lilies— blossom-like patterns of slush which float on the water— and enormous snow islands drift before the winds.

By mid-January this disintegration process is usually far advanced, though summer continues through most of February. But whereas the dissolution of the pack is gradual, its rebirth may be almost instantaneous. Within forty-eight hours of a flash freeze the pack may be as bad as it ever will become.

There is no way of predicting its condition in any particular season. Records for the past century show great variations in the depth and width of the Ross Sea pack, the most extensive in the Antarctic. In 1841, for example, Sir James Clark Ross's wooden ships, the *Erebus* and *Terror,* found no pack at all. The next year they were obliged to maneuver back and forth for eight hundred miles before they were able to get through the ice to open water. The Japanese ship *Kainan Maru* encountered no ice in December, 1911. On Admiral Byrd's second expedition in 1933 his ships proceeded to the Bay of Whales entirely through iceberg-studded open water. But other expeditions have been forced to buck up to four hundred miles of almost unbroken ice, and the Navy ships broke all records in going through a six-hundred-mile pack.

Admiral Byrd believes that these differences from year to year may not be as great as the records would indicate—that every year an open-water lane extends most of the way to the edge of the Ross Shelf. Its location, however, changes from summer to summer and precious time would be lost hunting for it over a five-hundred-mile front with ship and plane. The break might not be apparent for a hundred miles or more below the northern edge of the ice.

The great integrated ice systems are driven northward and westward by prevailing winds, surface currents, and the earth's rotation until they meet a belt of strong winds blowing from the west somewhere below the Antarctic Circle—usually between the 40th and 60th parallels. This produces an impasse. Movement of the packs is brought to an abrupt halt while the icebergs, propelled by deeper and more powerful currents, crash through and continue northward. It is impossible to approach the continent from any direction at any time without encountering this ice girdle. While generally continuous, it consists of a half-dozen or more closely integrated systems, each with its own nerve centers and patterns of behavior depending on the contours of the continent and the local distribution of currents and winds.

The Antarctic packs are unique both in magnitude and

behavior. In the north polar seas great ice fields are encountered which superficially show many of the same characteristics, but these cover land-circled seas and are relatively stationary. Crews of ships trapped in such a pack nearly always can make their way across the ice to land, proceeding in just about any direction. Even in midwinter, life is relatively abundant. The drift of the Antarctic pack, however, "is around and outward from a central land mass toward the stormiest seas in the world." A party isolated here is in the jaws of a trap from which there is no escape, unless by a rescue expedition. Northward is the tempestuous ocean in which no open boat can survive. Southward is a belt of open water across which rise unscalable walls of ice.

In the extreme complexity and integration of its behavior an ice pack might be compared with a vast living organism. Study of its movements is a study in inanimate rock-and-water psychology. Ice packs are explained, as far as they are understood at present, in the Navy's sailing directions for Antarctic waters:

Sea ice, when newly formed, is highly plastic and readily conforms to stresses. It acquires brittleness with age and reaches a state of strain where only a slight impulse may be required to break it. This impulse is usually provided by the wind. Strain cracks may be produced by a swell from the open sea moving under a large ice field. The floe, suspended between the crests of the swell, will be unsupported over the trough and a crack parallel to the wave front may result. This tendency to crack is always present in an ice field, whether composed of young ice or hummock floe. All cracks are due to relief of strain produced by stresses set up by sudden differences of temperature, unequal loading, or by pressure. But although cracks may be due to relief of stress within the pack while in motion, they also are a factor in allowing movement of the pack. Smaller floes are the product of cracks and, under the influence of the wind, these floes constantly shift their relative position, thereby producing leads or lanes which make the pack navigable.

The rate at which the different floes travel is not so much dependent on the size and depth of the floe as upon the nature of its surface. Since the pack is made up of a conglomeration of young ice, old floes which have not been subjected to pressure, and icebergs, each of these elements presents radically different resistance to wind and current. Surface irregularities, such as hummocks and pressure ridges, act as sail areas. A progeny of previous pressure, hummocked floes in turn become the cause of still further pressure. When two floes are moving at different rates, either the distance between them is increased and a lead or lane produced, or the distance is decreased, resulting in physical contact. In gaining momentum, larger floes will take longer to reach speed but, once underway, they will continue in motion long after smaller floes have become stationary. In early stages, therefore, the large, heavy floe will be charged by smaller floes overtaking it. In later stages it will itself be the attacker of smaller floes in its path. Due to their size and weight, the smaller floes will be disrupted, thereby creating new possibilities of yet further differences in speed.

Pack ice always drifts with the wind but slightly to the left of the true wind and the velocity of the drift does not depend entirely on the strength of the wind, since it is influenced greatly by the presence or absence of open water in the direction of the drift, even though the open water may be somewhat distant.

Disintegration of pack ice is produced almost entirely by the sea. Decay of the pack is due chiefly to mechanical attrition by the swell. The physical erosion of the floes produces scaling, resulting in the formation of bergy bits and brash. These become drift ice and move faster to destruction, while the scaling process enables the sea to reach more extensive areas.

Curious phenomena make their appearance as the cold advances in mid-February. When salt water freezes quickly, particles of salt separate on top of the ice. The moisture in the air crystallizes around the particles and creates fernlike forms about six inches high, known as frost flowers. These are so fragile that a slight breeze will shatter one of them into hundreds of pieces.

In the intervals of darkness around midnight false sunrises and false sunsets appear, like arches in the sky opposite the sun; sometimes they show all the colors of the rainbow and sometimes only vivid greens, blues, and purples. Across the sky float iridescent clouds, one of the most striking of all Antarctic sights—downy blue masses with banded margins of vivid purple, orange, and green.

Bright spots, often tinged with color, appear on a line parallel to the horizon at the same elevation as the sun. These are "mock suns," or parhelia; there are sometimes five or six of them at the same time. Prismatic sunrises and sunsets appear as high arches, with the colors of the spectrum extending from the top of the arch to the horizon, in the sky opposite the sun.

Creation Re-enacted

The span of human life in the Antarctic becomes a major interval instead of a fraction of a second in geological time. Here one observes the creation of the visible world; here one sees mountains born and watches them pass away.

Antarctica is a continent of ice—and ice is rock. It is plastic rock, as was the hot surface of the planet two billion years ago. Solid water differs from other rocks basically because it has an extremely low melting point, changing into a liquid at zero degrees centigrade while a thousand degrees of heat, for example, are necessary to liquefy granite.

Rockies and Himalayas rose out of what were deep ocean troughs 200 million years ago and Alps and Appalachians have subsided into ocean bottoms. Andes of yesterday may be pampas of tomorrow. But all these processes proceed at an extremely slow rate. In terms of the lifetime of a man, or the lifetime of the whole human race, hills and valleys are eternal with changes of only fractions of inches in generations. But the ice shell around the South Pole is a world in a visible state of flux where one may watch the piling up of mountains in a few months or a few years by almost precisely the same processes that elsewhere require millions of years. Here, where geological phenomena are speeded ten-thousandfold, it is possible to observe changes with the naked eye from month to month.

The mass of billions upon billions of tons that make up the continental icecap flows in all directions like tough dough under the pressure of its own accumulating weight. With all these quadrillions of tons of pressure pushing it from behind it is piled up against great granite and sandstone mountains and against converging streams of ice into enormous pressure ridges which are miniature mountain ranges.

Thus the ice land becomes a telescope for exploring terrestrial time. By watching the piling up of these blue frozen-water mountains geologists have an example of how the crust of the world came to have its present contours. Here is a vast natural laboratory of earth processes where nature carries out experiments with forces of such magnitude that they are equalled elsewhere only in mountain movements themselves.

A few miles from the Bay of Whales, in the winter of 1947, was a fairyland miniature of the Jura Mountains of Switzerland. It covered an area of about five square miles and was created by the piling up of ice as one stream flowing downward across the shelf came in contact with another. Peaks of luminous blue ice 150 feet high loom over deep canyons and crevassed valleys. The spectacle had come into existence since the first expedition under

Admiral Byrd established a camp near by and it is expected to endure about four more years before increasing pressure from the east pushes it into the sea. The mountain chain may be broken off in one great chunk, in which case it will drift north through the pack ice of the Ross Sea as a gigantic iceberg, finally to melt in the warmer waters of the South Pacific.

Dr. Arthur D. Howard, Navy expedition geologist, who had made previous geological studies in the Juras, said that the likeness was uncanny. It was possible to match—with a little imagination, of course—individual peaks and valleys. Yet the replica was built by the same processes as the Juras—which are at least a hundred million years old—in less than a generation.

The miniature range is beautiful, but it is a death trap for the unwary and certainly the most dangerous area in the Bay of Whales region. It can be entered with reasonable safety only by four men walking in single file and roped together. The area is full of deep crevasses hidden by light snow bridges, making necessary step-by-step progression and constant probing ahead with steel-speared pikes. On most days its approaches are veiled in Antarctica's weird white darkness which hides ice walls ahead until one bumps into them head-on. The way also is blocked with ice ridges fifty feet high for which special glacier climbing equipment is necessary.

Within the strange valleys one is in a world of mystic blueness. An eerie blue light suffuses the fantastic landscape; mouths of great blue caverns penetrating the ice cliffs for unknown distances open on every hand. Even aside from the hidden crevasses, though, it is a region of constant peril. Among the ice cliffs lurk sea leopards, the fierce flesh-eating seals of the ice shelf, which can waddle on their flippers as fast as the average man can run. An individual would have little chance with one of these monsters across the crevassed ice unless he were able to kill his pursuer with a first lucky shot. The region is also notable as being the southernmost extension of mammal life on earth. Beside the crevasses are great herds of the sluggish, harmless Weddell seals whose young are frequent victims of the sea leopards.

Not only is ice a mineral, differing chiefly from other kinds of rock in its low melting point, but it might be considered a whole family of minerals. Its properties vary considerably with age and with the pressures and temperatures to which it is subjected. A mineralogist finds a wide gulf between the glittering, hard blue ice of some sections of the continental plateau and the soft frozen water filled with air pockets which makes up the Ross Sea pack. Among the jobs of the expedition geologist was to bring back to Washington samples of different kinds of Antarctic "ice rock," immersed in gasoline in an electric refrigerator, to form part of the mineral collection of the U. S. Geological Survey.

When water solidifies, its molecules arrange themselves in the form of crystals of many forms and sizes, varying according to the speed of the freezing process and the degree of cold. Often the shapes are extremely beautiful. Navy expedition geologists made collections of these crystals—glittering little crucifixes, diamonds and the like —study of which may throw considerable light on the basic crystallization process by which liquids everywhere are converted into solids.

In a pit dug and blasted thirty-five feet deep into the barrier ice, with a constant temperature of several degrees below zero, Dr. Arthur Howard was able to observe the birth processes of the ice ages. This pit was first sunk about twenty-five feet below the surface of the névé by geologists of the previous expedition seven years earlier. Since then about eighteen feet of snow had accumulated over the surface at a rate of nearly three feet each winter.

Dr. Howard found that the depth of the original pit had been reduced about six feet as a result of the tremendous downward pressure of this accumulating weight. The scientists of the former expedition had bored auger holes in the wall of the pit, in the form of nearly perfect circles. Howard found the circles flattened into ellipses, with those near the top of the pit showing the greatest flattening. Before leaving, he drove spikes into the wall of the pit precisely one foot apart. Scientists of a future expedition will investigate this again in four or five years, and the lessened distances between the spikes will indicate the precise amount of compression undergone by the ice.

Here, apparently, is an explanation of glaciers and of the great ice ages which sweep over the earth every few tens of thousands of years. The snow of one winter, which for some reason escapes melting during the summer, weighs down on the snow of the preceeding winter, and eventually compresses it into ice. This in turn presses down on the previously formed ice beneath it. Obviously the process cannot be continued indefinitely, however, or ice would become infinitely dense and hard. At some point it begins to flow like putty under its own weight and if no obstacle is in the way a glacier results which gathers force through centuries until finally it becomes an irresistible tide of ice sweeping northward or southward over everything in its path. Antarctica presumably is in the middle of one of these great ice ages.

This same pit may furnish geologists with an ice-age gauge by which very precise measurements will determine whether ice formation is accelerating or declining; considerable light will also be thrown on the exact pressures necessary before this curious cold white sand, peculiar to both polar regions, changes into soft blue rock.

Nobody knows the thickness of the Antarctic icecap. It has been built up over a period of at least ten million years —some parts of it, indeed, may be as much as a hundred million years old. Only the highest mountain peaks jut over the surface of this billowy ocean of water-rock.

There are various means of determining the depth of this solid sea and deducing the contour of the land underneath. Perhaps the most accurate is by means of artificially propagated earthquake waves which move at different speeds through different materials. This requires time and infinite labor, however, and very few such measurements could be carried out in any one season; even a systematic survey of those limited areas of the continental icecap now accessible to land parties would require many years.

The recent Navy expedition had the benefit of a remarkable geophysical instrument, until the end of the war one of the most closely guarded of war secrets—the airborne magnetometer, which was used for rapid surveys of large areas of ocean for submerged, lurking submarines.

This was a Navy invention, conceived and perfected during the war at the Naval Ordnance Laboratory in Washington. With the war's end it was taken over by the U. S. Geological Survey and proved of extraordinary value in locating buried geological features indicative of oil-bearing country. The instrument did not locate oil; it merely indicated that the rock structure was such that petroleum might be present. It differentiated among the three major types of rocks—igneous, sedimentary, and metamorphic—which make up the earth's crust, and gave a picture of the contours in which they were arranged below the surface.

The air-borne magnetometer is said to start where radar leaves off. It makes possible the survey of the depth of ice as rapidly as an airplane can fly over the terrain, and these measurements are reasonably accurate. It detects variations in the earth's magnetic field, and of such variations as occur with discontinuity of structure, such as a hill, mountain, or deep valley under the ice. Magnetic intensity is measured in units known as "gammas"; that of the earth varies from twenty-five to seventy thousand gammas with different latitudes. Normal intensity over most of the surface of the globe has been determined with fair accuracy. The magnetometer detects variations of as little as a single gamma and reveals instantly any abnormality in the land over which it is used.

This apparatus was used in four flights over the ice shelf from the Little America base by Dr. James R. Balsley of the U. S. Geological Survey. To eliminate the magnetic effect of the plane itself the detector element of the magnetometer was contained in a streamlined, bombshaped casing known as the "bird" which was towed behind and beneath the aircraft on a cable one hundred feet long. Dr. Balsley was able to show rather conclusively that it would be possible in this way to map at least the rough contour of the land under the Antarctic icecap. His work was intended only as a demonstration, upon which future expeditions can base more extensive programs.

Near the eastern edge of the Ross Shelf are two large islands. One is Roosevelt Island; the other is a somewhat smaller mass of ice-covered rock slightly to the south. The two together are believed to constitute the fulcrum upon which two converging ice shelves turn. Hitherto the location and even the existence of the second island had been matters of deduction, but Balsley's magnetometer recordings showed unmistakably that it is a real body of land and, like Roosevelt Island, is composed chiefly of granite. Another island of similar size, shown on maps at the entrance to a small inlet slightly to the southwest of this island, appeared on this single flight either not to exist or to be composed of sedimentary rocks.

Balsley made one flight over the Rockefeller Mountains east of the Ross Sea, a chaos of low peaks which were discovered by Admiral Byrd in 1929. They are a geological anomaly since they bear no discernible relation to other mountain systems in this part of Antarctica. The magnetometer showed that they were composed largely of granite-like rocks, which agreed with the few specimens collected by land expeditions. On the other hand it was demonstrated conclusively that Mount LaGorce, about sixty miles east of the Rockefeller range, was composed almost entirely of sedimentary rock and therefore did not form a part of the same system. Balsley also discovered several changes in the shoreline of the Ross Shelf itself, as shown on existing maps. It is extremely difficult, even for a ground party, to tell where land begins in this region of endless ice, and the eastern edge was found at the point flown over to be about twenty miles east of the position assigned to it. Another source of special satisfaction was the finding of magnetic intensity variations in the neighborhood of Kainan Bay on the eastern shore of the Ross Sea, indicating an island which had been predicted on the basis of crevasse formation.

The presence of precious minerals under Antarctica is almost a foregone conclusion—such a large part of the earth's surface could hardly exist without gold, silver, platinum, uranium, etc., somewhere in its rocks. Perhaps it will never be worth the labor to search for them but the magnetometer can, at least, give a fair indication of where to look; it can locate the geological structures where they are most likely to be found.

The science of magnetism, which has played a prominent role in every polar survey, was represented on the Navy expedition by Dr. H. H. Howe and Lieutenant C. A. Schoene, both of the U. S. Coast and Geodetic Survey. Their base camp was located about five hundred miles from the South Magnetic Pole, which must be considered as the mathematical center of a region, probably a thousand square miles or more in area, where the compass needle on a vertical axis points straight down. In the Arctic this is a very large elliptical area which has been explored by numerous expeditions, but practically nothing is known of the extent or shape of the southern region—the last Byrd expedition placed it, by calculation, about two hundred miles from the place determined by Sir Douglas Mawson fifteen years before. It is known that the magnetic area, especially in the north, shifts considerably in a period of time and is difficult to locate with much precision, since the direction of a compass needle is dependent on the distribution of magnetic material in the neighborhood. It is, however, certain that the South Magnetic Pole is several thousand miles distant from the point on the Antarctic Continent exactly opposite the North Magnetic Pole.

The evidence gathered by Howe and Schoene indicated that the magnetic area had shifted very little from its position of seven years before. They found that the magnetic attraction was declining in intensity—an unexplained phenomenon that has been noted in the past generation over most of the earth.

Physical properties of ice were studied by experts of the Naval Research Laboratory, using as their chief tools the world's fastest echoes. Sound bounces back and forth through ice at a speed of nearly nine thousand feet a second, compared with a rate of a little over a thousand feet a second through air; the speed varies with different densities of ice, thus affording a means of determining the structure of this strange "rock" at various levels. Some of the principles developed might have far-reaching wartime application in detecting submarine sneak attacks beneath the ice, for although elaborate water detection methods were developed in the last war, the effect of an ice canopy over a sea wolf pack—possibly approaching over the top of the world by way of the North Pole—has remained largely unknown. The region around Little America provided an ideal testing ground, with great depths of water under great thicknesses of ice. Explosions on the shelf produced double echoes, one from the water surface showing the ice thickness, and one from the sea floor showing the depth of the underlying sea.

A curious anomaly revealed by the echoes is that there is usually a thin layer of water between ice and land, producing a type of echo that is very difficult to detect and determine. This layer is believed formed by the melting effect of the enormous downward pressure of the overlying ice, and serves as a sort of lubricated surface over which glaciers slide.

The South Pole

The South Pole, the mathematical bottom of the world, is in the middle of a depression, about five hundred feet deep, very close to the center of the great polar plateau. This point, above which the sun stands still through most of the ninety-day Antarctic summer, has been reached four times by man—twice by land and twice by air. The pole has absolutely no distinguishing characteristic in the seemingly infinite desolation of whiteness. On his last flight, however, Admiral Byrd reported that the sastrugi—wind-piled windrows of snow which cover the plateau—seemed a little less prominent there, indicating milder winds, and all who have reached the pole have reported excellent weather. It may be that this particular spot lies beyond the tempests.

Attainment of the mathematical point where every direction is north is no longer of any particular scientific interest, but the pole will remain for all time a symbol of human courage and endurance. There, within a few days of each other in the Antarctic summer of 1911-12, arrived the Norwegian sailor, Roald Amundsen, and the British naval officer, Sir Robert Falcon Scott, after a dramatic race through a vast unknown of haunted blizzards. For one the race ended in death. To the other it brought only a continuation of lifelong frustration.

This was a race between two strikingly different personalities.

The Englishman was a bundle of contradictions. He was so absent-minded that he once got up at midnight to attend a dinner for which he had dressed earlier in the evening and then gone to bed, having completely forgotten his important engagement. He was a hard disciplinarian and a strict taskmaster, liable to temper tantrums, and a bad judge of human nature. He was a sentimentalist who would burst into tears at virtually any sad story or strain of music, or snatch of gospel hymn. He had weak lungs and tired easily; he could not endure the sight of blood nor could he stand to see dogs whipped, a trait which may have contributed in the end to his tragic failure. He was a mystic who went into lyric ecstasies as he read spirit messages in the flickering curtains of the southern lights. As a cadet he was called "old moony" because of his daydreaming and despaired of as a future naval officer. He was described as a lazy boy, untidy to the point of slovenliness, with a fierce, uncontrollable temper.

All his adult life he made a fetish of conquering physical weakness. He was the sternest of self-disciplinarians who viewed as deadly sins his constantly outcropping sentimentality, his erratic emotions, his debauches of poetic dreaming. He forced himself, despite the sickness he felt at the sight of blood, to watch his expedition surgeon cutting up seals in puddles of gore. In England he purchased a large dog, too powerful to be restrained by a leash, which he took with him on his daily walks so that he would be forced to run to keep up with the animal. The purpose was not entirely to keep in good physical condition but to prevent him from giving way to the temptation of laziness.

This picture of the explorer is derived largely from accounts of his closest friend, the godfather of his children, to whom he addressed his last letter when he was dying of cold, starvation, and hurt pride in a blizzard on the Ross Shelf—Sir James Barrie, the noted author. Few men understood each other better than the two mystics who followed such different roads in the world.

Scott, then a thirty-five-year-old Royal Navy captain, led his first Antarctic expedition under the auspices of the Royal Geographic Society in 1901. After an easy passage through the Ross Pack his wooden ship *Discovery* was frozen in at McMurdo Sound for the winter. This expedition accomplished little, but the commander returned to England with the virus of the green southern lights in his blood and the determination to be the first man to stand at the bottom of the world. Appealing to the patriotism of Englishmen and obtaining a small government grant, he succeeded in raising funds for the purchase of the large Dundee whaler *Terra Nova* and in enlisting a group of able scientists and sailors.

Scott reached Melbourne on October 12, 1910. There he heard for the first time that the Norwegian explorer Roald Amundsen, first man to sail through the Northwest Passage and an Antarctic veteran who had served as mate on a Belgian expedition twelve years before, also was on his way to the Ross Sea and planned a sledge dash to the South Pole.

A far different, but equally frustrated, character was the man who was fated to win the tragic race.

The dream of discovering the North Pole had dominated Amundsen's life from the time he read of the exploits of British and American expeditions which braved the Arctic in the forties and fifties in search of the lost English explorer Sir John Franklin. With an unshakable singleness of purpose virtually every act of his life was directed toward standing on the top of the world. He flew over it at long last, but with only a brief glimpse of the long-sought goal far below. Most men who knew him agreed that to the day he crashed to his death on a rescue mission over the Arctic north of Spitsbergen, Amundsen was a thwarted, unhappy man. He never considered the South Pole more than a stepping-stone to the North Pole.

As a youth he had rebelled at working in his father's shipping office at Oslo. For two years he attended medical school at the urging of his mother, but without interest. Then, the first step on his way to the North Pole, he went to sea as a common sailor on a Norwegian freighter. In 1895 this ship put in at Antwerp, where Amundsen heard of a Belgian expedition to the Antarctic which was being organized, in the face of mounting financial difficulties, by a former artillery officer, Captain Adrien de Gerlache. The twenty-three-year-old Norwegian sailor, obtaining letters of introduction from his celebrated countryman Fridtjof Nansen, secured for himself the position of first mate.

For thirteen months the expedition's ship, the *Belgica*,

was frozen in the pack and drifted helplessly over the
fog-covered Sea of Bellingshausen. Scurvy and insanity
attacked the crew. Gerlache was incapacitated; Lieutenant
Danco, second in command, died, and Amundsen found
himself essentially in command.

The *Belgica* expedition provided Amundsen's education
as a polar explorer, but he thought of applying it only to
the great quest of his life at the other end of the earth.
He returned to Europe and established himself at Ham-
burg, where he purchased, largely with promissory notes,
the forty-seven-ton sloop *Gjoa* for a projected expedition
to the North Magnetic Pole. Promised contributions were
not forthcoming, however, and Amundsen was pestered
with note collectors. One morning the *Gjoa* and its crew
were missing—the explorer had fled from his creditors toward the open sea where they could not follow him. For
three years they were left to worry about their money.

During this time Amundsen sailed through the Northwest Passage, thus finally bringing the dreams of the
Cabots, Frobisher, and Henry Hudson to reality. Incidentally, he "fixed the position" of the magnetic pole, a
claim which experts on the earth's magnetism would smile
at today. It is noteworthy that Amundsen, like his great
contemporary, Sir Ernest Shackleton, was cynical in his
relations to science. He never evidenced any devotion to it
except when he was attempting to raise money. To him
adventure, wild beauty in action, was its own excuse.

By lecturing, writing, and collecting on promises
Amundsen was able to settle the debts from which he had
fled. The time had come for the greatest adventure of all
—to sail northward in the Arctic explorer Nansen's old

ship, the *Fram*, allow himself to be frozen in the ice, and drift across the North Pole. It would cost a great deal of money.

Again Amundsen went begging with pleas "for the sake of science." This time, because of his larger reputation, the gods of the marketplace were kinder, but still funds were forthcoming with discouraging reluctance. Then, in 1909, came a crushing blow—news that the American, Admiral Robert E. Peary, had planted the Stars and Stripes on the top of the world.

Amundsen met this with the most astounding move in the history of exploration. He was still ill-financed, ill-staffed, ill-equipped. But the *Fram* was in seaworthy condition, and, confiding his intentions only to his brother, he set sail, presumably in conformity with the plans outlined to his backers. The *Fram* went south instead of north. At Madeira the captain told his crew the real situation—they were on their way to the South Pole.

His reasoning was even more surprising than the decision itself: If he could reach the bottom of the world the publicity value would be so great that he would have no trouble raising fresh funds to resume his expedition to the top of the world. Otherwise he counted the attainment of the South Pole as of no importance; the Antarctic was simply a barrier to be crossed on the way to the Arctic.

When Amundsen made his extraordinary decision he was well aware that Scott was on the point of sailing south, but he rationalized the situation to his own satisfaction. Discovery of the South Pole, he said, was only one of the announced objectives of the British and, to judge from previous announcements, not the chief one; the expedition had a quite varied program of exploration and scientific research upon which he had not the slightest intention of intrusion. His single purpose was to reach the pole and return to civilization as soon as possible.

Thus the stage was set for one of the epic tragedies of history.

Scott encountered a far more difficult pack on his second trip and was greatly delayed in reaching McMurdo Sound, where he established the expedition's base camp on Cape Evans. While the camp was being set up the *Terra Nova* skirted eastward along the barrier edge to the Bay of Whales. There the commander's worst fears were confirmed. Amundsen had already arrived in the *Fram,* and his men were busy building Framheim, the base camp near Little America. The Norwegians were sixty-nine miles closer to the pole than the British at Cape Evans.

Clearly it was to be a race for glory between two explorers and two flags.

The winter night closed down on the rival camps and both parties toed the mark for a head start as soon as the sun rose again over the hummocked ice. Amundsen finally got underway on October 19, 1911. Scott started from McMurdo Sound thirteen days later. He planned to follow rather closely the path onto the high continental plateau which had been blazed a few years earlier by his former associate, Ernest Shackleton.

Scott's plan looked excellent on paper. He proposed to advance toward the pole by easy stages with two supporting parties, laying down a supply depot with sufficient food and fuel for six weeks every sixty-five miles along the 922-mile route.

At the outset all the supplies were to be carried on motor sledges. In these the commander had little confidence; they bogged down in the snow and were essentially useless in areas of rough ice and crevasses. However they could be expected to bear most of the load for the first stages of the trip over the smooth surface of the shelf and could be sent back after the remaining supplies had been reloaded on sledges drawn by Manchurian ponies. Two dog teams accompanied the expedition for emergencies.

The ponies were expected to haul the supplies to the foot of the great Beardmore glacier, probably Antarctica's mightiest ice river, which forms a broad highway between towering mountain ranges to the polar plateau. Each pony dragged 650 pounds; once a cache was set up the animal was to be killed and its flesh stored to augment the food supply. When the mouth of the Beardmore was reached the last pony was to be slaughtered and the second supporting party sent back with the dogs. On the trek up the glacier and across the plateau the remaining supplies were to be hauled on hand-drawn sledges by the four men chosen to accompany Scott to the pole.

Bad luck dogged the realization of this program. Three of the ponies drowned when sea ice broke up beneath them near Cape Evans before the start of the polar dash. In the middle of the shelf the party was marooned in a four-day blizzard, followed by unprecedented warm weather with the temperature barely at the freezing point. The ice surface was covered with slush eighteen inches deep.

Through this Antarctic morass the party waded and wallowed for fourteen days.

On December 16, nearly seven weeks after the start from Cape Evans and long after the last pony had been slaughtered, hard "blue ice" was reached at an elevation of three thousand feet up the glacier. Thenceforth the pace was more rapid and the polar party emerged on the plateau, 6,800 feet above the level of the Ross Shelf, five days later.

On January 4 the last supporting party turned back and Scott with his four companions started the final lap of their outward journey, a distance which they estimated at about 145 miles. Skies were clear and weather excellent . . . the men had every reason to believe that their hard luck had run out. Of even more significance, they felt that they had won the race with Amundsen; they had seen no trace of the Norwegians along the trail. The flag of England would be the first at the bottom of the world.

They were due for a rude awakening. Less than sixty miles from the South Pole, after crossing latitude 88, Scott's party came upon fresh sledge tracks. There could be only one interpretation: Their rivals were at least several days ahead of them. Their seventy-five days of weary, painful trudging over barrier, glacier, and plateau had been in vain. A little later, on January 17, they sighted a tent above which flew the flag of Norway. Inside the tent Amundsen had left a letter for Scott, together with an account of his exploit to be forwarded to the king of Norway that his triumph might be recognized in the event he himself perished on the return journey to Framheim. He had written:

Polheim
15 December, 1911

Dear Capt. Scott:

As you are probably the first to reach this area after us I will ask you kindly to forward this letter to King Haakon VII. If you can use any of the articles left in this tent please do not hesitate to do so. The sledge left outside may be of use to you. With best regards I wish you safe return.

Yours truly,

Roald Amundsen

Perhaps no man ever suffered a more bitter disillusion than did Scott at the South Pole on January 18, 1912. The proof of his rival's triumph was indisputable; Amundsen had won the race with less planning, less expense, less equipment. The Englishman could not understand, and did not when he died, how it had been done. For him the flag of the Norwegians was the banner of death. He was far behind schedule and even with the best of luck his party could not hope to reach the shelter of Cape Evans, more than nine hundred miles away, before the onset of the Antarctic autumn with its rapidly lengthening black nights and blizzards.

Scott lingered only long enough to fix the precise position of the bottom of the earth. The spot agreed upon was less than a half-mile from that established by Amundsen—a remarkable example of the accuracy of both men, considering the difficulty of solar observation in the Antarctic.

With heavy hearts the five Englishmen started their

return journey on January 19, wearily dragging their heavy sledge behind them through the sandlike snow which covers the plateau.

It was an uphill road away from the pole; the mathematical southernmost point of the world lies in a five-hundred-foot depression in the surface of the plateau. The heavy haul was especially difficult because of the thin air at an altitude of ten thousand feet above sea level. Add to this the fact that the men were already badly weakened by the hardships they had experienced and had been brought to a nerve-shattering climax by the sight of Amundsen's flag.

Four of the party were tough little men—physically, mentally, and morally tough and resilient. The fifth, Petty Officer Edgar Evans of the British Navy, was a two-hundred-pound six-footer and a veteran sledge man. He had been the wheelhorse of the expedition, the man always called for when any job required exceptional physical strength; because of this he was picked especially for the polar dash. This probably was one of Scott's worst mistakes. Had he chosen a small man there is at least a possibility that the party might have returned safely. Paradoxical as it may seem, history shows rather clearly that big, strong men are not well equipped to be explorers —they seldom show the stamina necessary in emergencies.

Almost from the start of the return trip Evans, who until then had been a cheery fellow, began to complain and drop behind. It was obvious to the others that he was breaking fast; the man was sick. His feet and hands were badly frostbitten. He no longer could pull his share of the burden and finally had to be relieved altogether. Very

likely this unhappy change could be interpreted as due to
food deficiency; Evans could not fuel his big body on the
rations sufficient for the smaller men.

Then came the day when he stumbled on the hummocked ice of the Beardmore glacier and sustained a brain
concussion. There was an emergency council. By this time
all realized that the chances of getting back alive were
very small at best, and essentially non-existent if the party
was burdened with a sick man; the decision, however, was
not to abandon Evans. The tent was pitched and Scott
reconciled himself to a long and probably fatal delay until
the sailor was able to travel again. But that night the in-
jured man died without regaining consciousness, thus giving his companions one more chance to push ahead. It
grew colder and colder as they stumbled and staggered
toward the mouth of the Beardmore through white darkness and blizzard. All now suffered intensely from frost-
bite and were constantly growing weaker. It was then that
Scott ordered the medical officer and second in command
of the party, Dr. E. A. Wilson, whose accomplishments on
the expedition rate second only to those of the commander
himself, to do what they had agreed upon from the beginning if the worst came—distribute the opium tablets. If
anyone felt he could endure no more he had only to swallow one of these white pills and fall into a sleep from
which he would not wake.

The man now in the worst physical condition was
Captain L. E. G. Oates of the British Army. His feet and
hands were frozen and at times he became delirious. In
these last hours he thought bitterly that he had brought

the disgrace of failure on the regiment he represented—
the ultra-swanky Iniskillin Dragoons. He knew also that
he was a burden, and would constantly become a worse
burden, on the others. He continually asked the doctor's
advice.

"Slog on, keep slogging on," was all Wilson could
answer.

One night when the four were holed up in the tent during a blizzard, Oates told the others he was going for a
walk. He stepped out in the storm and was never seen
again. The men knew his purpose and did not try to stop
him.

The three survivors, Scott, Dr. Wilson, and Lieutenant
H. R. Bowers of the British Marines, crawled heroically
on over the crevassed ice. Their one remaining hope was
to reach One Ton Camp, a cache of food and fuel left on
the shelf about halfway between the mouth of the Beardmore and their home base.

Oates had died on March 17, his birthday. The others
crept forward two or three more days, covering about
twenty miles. Their supplies were nearly exhausted. They
still had eleven miles to go when a blizzard broke around
them and they pitched their tent for the last time. Even
if they had been able to reach the supply depot it is doubtful if they could have gone farther; their feet were frozen
now.

So when they crawled into the tent there was little
doubt in their minds that it would be their grave. Perhaps
they were not too uncomfortable in their last hours. Their
sleeping bags were stiff with ice which melted with the

warmth of their bodies as long as any warmth was left and the canvas protected their faces from the screaming blizzard outside.

How long they survived in the tent nobody knows—ten or eleven days at best. Scott remained busy to the last. He wrote letters to Dr. Wilson's wife and to Lieutenant Bowers' mother in England. For himself he wrote to Sir James Barrie:

We are in a desperate state, feet frozen, etc. No fuel and a long way from food, but it would do your heart good to be in our tent, to hear our songs and the cheery conversation as to what we will do when we get to Hut Point.

Later: We are very near the end but have not and will not lose good cheer. We have had four days of storm in our tent and nowhere's food and fuel. We did intend to finish ourselves when things proved like this but we have decided to die naturally in the track.

One of the dying explorer's last acts was to scribble with frozen fingers the following apology to his countrymen for what he regarded as his failure as a British empire builder:

The causes of the disaster are not due to faulty organization, but to misfortune in all risks which had to be undertaken.

The loss of pony transport in March, 1911, obliged me to start later than I had intended and obliged the limits of the stuff to be transported to be narrowed.

The weather throughout the outward journey, and especially the long gale in 83 south, stopped us. We fought these untoward events with a will and conquered, but it cut into our provision reserves.

Every detail of our food supplies, clothing, and depots made on the interior ice sheet and over that long stretch of nine hundred miles to the pole and back worked out to perfection. The advance party should have returned to the glacier in fine form and with a surplus of food but for the astonishing failure of the man whom we had least expected to fail. Edgar Evans was thought the strongest man of the party.

The Beardmore glacier is not difficult in fine weather but on our return we did not get a single completely fine day; this, with a sick companion, enormously increased our difficulties. As I have said elsewhere, we got into frightfully rough ice and Edgar Evans received a concussion of the brain—he died a natural death but left us a shaken party with the season unduly advanced.

But all the facts enumerated above were as nothing compared to the surprise that awaited us on the barrier. I maintain that our arrangements for returning were quite adequate and that no one in the world would have expected the temperature and surfaces we encountered at this time of year. On the summit in latitude 85-86 we had minus 20, minus 30. On the barrier in latitude 82, 10,000 feet lower, we had minus 30 in the day, minus 47 at night pretty regularly, with a constant headwind during our day marches. It is clear that these circumstances came on very suddenly, and our wreck is certainly due to this sudden advent of severe weather which does not seem to have any satisfactory cause.

I do not think human beings ever came through such a month as we have come through and we should have got through in spite of the weather but for the sickening of a second companion, Captain Oates, and a shortage of fuel in our depots for which I cannot account, and finally but for the storm which had fallen upon us within thirteen miles of the depot at which I had hoped to secure final supplies. Surely misfortune could scarcely have exceeded this last blow.

We arrived within thirteen miles of One Ton Camp with fuel for one hot meal and food for two days. For four days we have been unable to leave the tent—the gale howling about us. We are weak, writing is difficult, but for my own sake I do not regret this journey, which has shown that Englishmen can endure hardships, help one another, and meet death with as great a fortitude as ever in the past. We took risks; we knew we took them; things have come out against us; and therefore we have no cause for complaint but bow to the will of Providence, determined still to do our best to the last.

But if we have been willing to give our lives to this enterprise which is for the honor of our country, I appeal to our countrymen to see that those who depend on us are properly cared for. Had we lived I should have had a tale to tell of the hardihood, courage, and endurance of my companions which would have stirred the heart of every Englishman. These rough notes and our dead bodies must tell the tale, but surely a great rich country like ours will see that those who are dependent on us are properly provided for.

R. SCOTT

Scott, Dr. Wilson, and Lieutenant Bowers died in the tent on the ice about 150 miles from the McMurdo Sound base on or about March 29. Eight months later, at the start of the Antarctic summer, a search party found the bodies, together with the commander's notes and diaries. These constitute the greatest of all epics of polar exploration.

Robert Falcon Scott had failed in his mission from his own time-circumscribed point of view. Through a series of adverse circumstances—perhaps, despite his dying protests, through his own inadequate preparations to some extent—he had been beaten in the race to the bottom of the world by a more practical and less temperamental man. But in the long sweep of history he had succeeded with a measure of success far greater than would have come with the mere attainment of a mathematical point on the surface of the globe before anybody else.

With their frozen footprints down the cascading ice of the mighty Beardmore, and across the ridged, crevassed barrier, Scott and his men wrote a story of human fortitude and heroism for which history shows few equals and which will be an inspiration for all who follow them.

Thirty-five years after the tragedy a U. S. Navy plane was soaring over the barrier on its way to explore the mountains west of the Ross Sea, many of which had been named by Scott but upon whose towering majesty he and his companions had only looked from afar.

It was uncomfortably warm in the cockpit. Lieutenant George H. Anderson, the pilot, started to raise a window.

"George," quietly remarked Commander William M. Hawkes, the commander of the flight, "do you realize that we are complaining about the heat almost exactly above the spot where a party of very brave men froze to death?"

Hawkes had been a lifelong admirer of Scott. To him this featureless, unmarked, and unmarkable spot in the great ice desert—longitude 169.15 east, latitude 79.38 south—was holy ground. He had kept careful watch for it ever since the mission had left Little America.

Thus men fly in relative comfort and safety today where Scott and his men crawled through the blizzard and the night to their doom.

The Norwegians made their first start for the pole on September 8 with eight men, seven sleds, and ninety dogs. After three days in blinding snow, with the temperature sinking at one time to 108 below zero Fahrenheit, they were obliged to turn back. From the failure, however, Amundsen gained invaluable experience. Impatiently he and his party waited at Framheim for signs of the Antarctic spring, the reappearance of birds and seals around the Bay of Whales. When the first of the colony of Weddell seals that live among the pressure ridges crawled out of their home in a crevasse he accepted the animals' judgment that winter was done. The second start was made on October 19, nearly two weeks before Scott was able to get underway with his sleds drawn by ponies. This time Amundsen and four companions went across the shelf with four sleds, each drawn by thirteen dogs. The sleds were lightly loaded. Provisions sufficient for four months already had been cached at the foot of the Axel Heiberg glacier.

Across the barrier and up the glacier they fought through fog and blizzard. Their ascent of the Axel Heiberg to the plateau was one of the most difficult feats yet accomplished by Antarctic explorers. It has sometimes been charged that Amundsen had all the luck with weather while Scott got all the bad breaks, but this was only partly true. One party met about as nasty weather as the other, but the Norwegians encountered it on their way to the pole when they were in good physical condition and spurred by enthusiasm, the Englishmen on their way back when they were exhausted from their long journey and low in spirits.

Once on the plateau, Amundsen's troubles were over. The party entered a period of sunny, almost windless days. Both the men and the remaining dogs were in excellent shape after their ordeal of crevasses and tempests. Perhaps most important of all, they found that their days of climbing were over; the ice sheet either was a level plain or, as proved the case as they neared the pole, it sloped gently downward.

Amundsen left as little to luck as possible. Snow beacons, to be used as guides on the way back, were set up

every three miles. A cache with provisions for four days
was left every sixty miles. For eleven days they moved
inland from the head of the Axel Heiberg. The average
day's march was about fifteen miles; one day they traveled
twenty-eight miles. On December 8 they crossed latitude
88 degrees, 88 minutes south, the farthest point attained
by Sir Ernest Shackleton three years earlier.

On the afternoon of December 14 they reached "the
spot where the sun stands still." This physical observation
entranced Amundsen: The solar disk was continuously
directly overhead. It was a bright day with a temperature
of 41 below zero. There were no signs of the Englishmen.
Amundsen felt briefly the high exultation that comes
with a great accomplishment—and then in the northern
heavens flashed his star. If he got back to civilization alive
he would be the greatest explorer in the world; what he
wanted would be his for the asking. In his mind he was
already halfway to the North Pole.

The Norwegians stayed four days at the earth's bottom,
fixing accurately the position of the pole. They raised the
Norse flag and named the entire continental plateau after
their sovereign, Haakon VII. They were 870 miles from
Framheim and had been fifty-seven days on the way. The
return journey was almost a picnic; weather continued
nearly perfect and they were able to observe Christmas
Eve on the glacier in high spirits, smoking cigars which
one member of the party had carried all the way to the
Pole for just this occasion. In thirty-eight days they were
back at their base, all in excellent condition and with no
further reason for remaining in the Antarctic. Meanwhile
Scott was struggling through blizzards on the Beardmore.

There has been endless debate on why the Norwegians succeeded while the more experienced English so dismally failed. The difference has been attributed to pure luck, to the fact that Amundsen relied entirely on dogs for transportation, to the shorter route, to the earlier start, to better planning. Probably all these played a part. But all are encompassed in the singleness of Amundsen's purpose—to get to the pole and back again in the shortest possible time.

He returned to Norway in 1913—again engaged in pursuit of the real ambition of his life which was to drift with the ice across the North Pole. This time he was thwarted by the start of World War I. Only in 1918 was he able to get underway in the specially constructed ship *Maud*, but the expedition was a failure—the ice did not drift according to his calculations. The war had brought aviation to the fore and on his fourth attempt in 1926 Amundsen crossed the pole, flying from Spitsbergen to Point Barrow, Alaska, in the semi-rigid dirigible *Norge*, built in Italy. He was accompanied by the American explorer Lincoln Ellsworth.

Demon Tempests

Observations of south polar weather are a major objective of any expedition to this part of the world. Unfortunately, however, most such observations in the past have been of too short duration to permit many conclusions—they have been made, for the most part, only outside the great bowl of the continental plateau which is inaccessible except for brief periods.

The South Pole is the Southern Hemisphere's brew vat of storms. Here is created much of the weather of the continents below the equator. A mass of billions upon billions of tons of heavy, cold air builds up constantly above the continental icecap, the coldest place on earth. The towering iceberg of atmosphere in the sub-stratosphere continuously spills over in wild torrents and careens northward in counter-clockwise whirling anti-cyclones, or "highs"; an almost everlasting wind blows downward from the top of the plateau, almost two miles in the sky, toward the unbroken northern ring of stormy seas. Everywhere, except toward Australia, it crashes against the broken rim of mountains. It is whirled westward with the revolutions of the spinning planet and ejected through cracks in the mountain wall, down broad rivers of ice, at velocities reaching a hundred miles an hour. Sweeping across the plateau, the great wind picks up bodily millions of tons of snow which it carries aloft and deposits over the pack ice.

At about the seas' edge the whirling high smashes into gentler, warmer, wetter air blown southward across the oceans, moving with a clockwise motion. This is the belt of "lows," and the meetingplace is a girdle of fog and swirling snow around the continent. The lows, or cyclones, are pressed northward against another belt of high pressure until the effects of a billiard-ball progression are felt as far as the equator. This of course is an over-simplification of the picture, because the actual pattern of Southern Hemisphere weather is extremely complex and little understood. The major difficulty is the lack of permanent weather stations on the plateau itself, where the building up of the great "high" could be followed from day to day, and around the rim of the continent where its breakthroughs could be recorded. This want may be filled in the next few years, with both Australia and New Zealand planning to set up observatories on the Antarctic coast.

The Antarctic Continent is a weather-making machine incomparably greater, with the large-scale phenomena it produces, than any other on the globe. Northern Hemisphere weather follows a vaguely similar pattern, with the Arctic basin the brew pot of the winter storms of North America, Europe, and Asia, but there, because of the ameliorating effects of the sea with its ice-covered islands, the building of highs is a less constant and more complex process. Out of the Arctic the great anti-cyclones flow uphill from ocean to continent, which is precisely the reverse of the Antarctic phenomenon.

For at least a generation reliable observatories, functioning twenty-four hours a day, have been stationed around the Arctic rim, and permanent stations are now being set up within the basin itself. Whenever a storm starts moving the entire hemisphere knows about it within a few hours and weather forecasters in Washington, London, and Moscow modify their predictions in accordance with the changing pattern.

Does any happening in the middle of the Antarctic ice-cap have an effect on the weather of the United States or Europe? This remains a debatable question and only within the past year has there been much evidence of an interlocking of the meteorological patterns of the Northern and Southern hemispheres. U. S. Weather Bureau scientists now have observed a periodical shifting of the weight of the atmosphere above the two hemispheres; the shifts amount to about ten trillion tons of air and may take place at intervals of a few days. This appears to affect quite profoundly the permanent westerly winds due to the earth's rotation—they tend to become stronger in the Northern Hemisphere when the weight of the atmosphere is least, which in turn has a profound effect on the prevalence of storms. Here is the first indication of a close relationship between Northern and Southern Hemisphere weather and makes conditions inside the Antarctic Circle significant—just how much so it is impossible to say as yet —to North America and Europe. Within this generation the stratosphere-scraping bowl of the Antarctic Continent may prove the key to reliable long-range weather forecasting.

Although the Navy expedition's meteorologists were concerned chiefly with local forecasting of conditions likely to be encountered on mountain flights, they developed considerable data of fundamental importance and observed some curious phenomena. They located, for example, two of the Antarctic's cyclone cradles. One is on the plateau, presumably not far from the South Magnetic Pole, which is one of the great vents for the eternal wind blowing northward. Warm north winds come from the Pacific across the Balleny Islands and "cyclones" are born which turn eastward and gather force rapidly over the Ross Sea. It is these cyclones which are largely responsible for the fantastic "frozen tempests" of the great ice pack. The other cyclone cradle is near Mount Ruth Siple, on the eastern edge of the Roosevelt Sea. Here polar air sweeps through a wide gap in the mountains to crash into the warm north winds; thus again storm-carrying cyclones are created which swing eastward and finally dissipate somewhere over the Palmer Peninsula just south of the South American continent.

The location of these cradles accounts for the origin of storms in two of the four quadrants into which Antarctica ordinarily is divided. It is a logical assumption that there are two undiscovered cyclone cradles for the other quadrants, perhaps serving as triggers for the weather of parts of Australia and Africa.

Strange phenomena and curious anomalies were also observed. One day, when the temperature was close to 15 below zero, perfect visibility was achieved for eight hours—it was possible to follow with the naked eye an observation

balloon to an altitude of 79,000 feet, where it disappeared
in a deep purple sky with a single star shining in broad
daylight. This was the planet Venus. The sky color was
described as one not previously recorded; it was the color
of the infinite coldness of outer space, and compared with
it the normal blue of the heavens seemed like a soft wool
blanket.

There were very rapid alterations in temperature, such
as a rise of 15 degrees in an hour, with no change in the
direction of the wind. This was considered a confirmation
of the air-mass hypothesis now almost universally used in
weather forecasting.

One of the most striking of Antarctic meteorological
phenomena is the permanent so-called "inversion layer."
Daily balloon soundings showed a fairly constant stratum
about three hundred feet thick and two thousand feet
above the earth's surface in which the temperature is 8 to
10 degrees higher than at ground level; one day an 18-
degree difference was found. Until this stratum is reached,
however, there is a steady temperature decline with altitude.
This same phenomenon is observed in middle latitudes but the temperature change usually is much less pronounced and ordinarily is found only immediately after
sunrise. Here this warm blanket in the sky persists twenty-
four hours a day during the summer. Above it the thermometer again declines steadily to a minimum of about
60 below zero at an altitude of 23,000 feet. This is the
floor of the Antarctic stratosphere, a region in which there
is no further decline of temperature with increasing height
during the summer months; an increase may even be reg-
istered for a few miles. During the winter months theo-

retically the stratosphere above the south polar regions drops to within about three thousand feet of sea level but it never has been possible to demonstrate with balloon soundings that this phenomenon actually takes place. Should it occur, Antarctica would literally be a "continent in the stratosphere."

Representatives of the U. S. Weather Bureau accompanying the Navy expedition brought into the Antarctic for the first time special devices making possible study of the winds over the low cloud cover of the continent to an altitude of about six miles. Such studies were conducted with balloons dragging targets which can be followed by radar—a method developed by the Army Air Forces during the war. The Weather Bureau observers also studied conditions to twelve thousand feet by means of radiosondes, remarkable robot messengers into space which automatically record and report wind directions and humidity by radio temperatures.

A chore of the expedition's meteorologists was bottling South Pole wind—the earth's richest and purest air—for analysis at the U. S. Bureau of Standards in Washington. Antarctic atmosphere is distinguished by a notably different mixture of gases than that normally breathed in middle latitudes, and especially near the equator. It contains about two per cent more nitrogen and slightly greater amounts of oxygen, and the rare inert gas, argon. The greatest difference is in water vapor, which constitutes almost three per cent of the air at the equator and only one-fifth of one per cent around the Bay of Whales. Antarctic air also contains a slightly greater content of carbon dioxide, the gas which is the basic building stone of living matter, though this is so conspicuously absent at the earth's bottom.

This air is curiously invigorating—perhaps attributable to its slightly different chemical composition and perhaps to its dryness and absolute purity. Over the plateau, however, it is quite rarefied; its altitude is greater than that reached by any mountaintop in the eastern United States. The thinness of the atmosphere is a bugaboo not only to pilots who are unable to attain altitude but to ground parties who become fatigued with relatively little effort, as is also true in the high Andes.

Around the Bay of Whales the mean yearly temperature is between minus 10 and minus 15 degrees Fahrenheit. On three or four occasions in midsummer the thermometer has risen to 40 degrees, while the minimum recorded there was minus 75 on September 5, 1940. Every winter, temperatures in the minus 70s have been observed close to the sea, which apparently has a great ameliorating effect. Little is known of the climatology of the interior. From late March to mid-August, 1934, Admiral Byrd occupied a station ninety-four miles to the southward, where he recorded a minimum temperature of minus 83 in mid-July and the thermometer reached the lower 70s several times. He found that temperatures ranged consistently from 10 to 20 degrees lower than at the base camp.

In the middle of the continent the cold must be much more intense, probably reaching well under 100 degrees below zero. The South Pole should be, and very likely is, also the pole of maximum cold. In the north the extreme temperature low was recorded not at the North Pole but on the Arctic coast of Siberia, about eight hundred miles to the south.

The land is literally a "snow desert." The everlasting wind blowing from the pole is as dry as winds over the Sahara; there is no rain, except during the summer months upon the Palmer Peninsula, and precipitation is entirely in the form of snow. Most of the snow which falls over the Bay of Whales region probably has been picked up by the blizzards from the surface of the névé.

This lack of precipitation is the chief factor operating to bring the Antarctic ice age to an end. Except near the coasts, it is quite unlikely that the icecap is becoming any thicker—it is constantly flowing outward through the mountain gaps and breaking off in the form of icebergs. If this movement should continue for a few more hundred thousand years the icecap may almost entirely disappear.

Mountain Ramparts

It will require a generation of geologists with easy access to their mysterious fastnesses to find a pattern in the helter-skelter distribution of the South Pole's rampart of mountains which front the seas. They curve, bend at sharp angles, crisscross each other. Some among them are very old mountains formed of Archean rocks which had hardened before life began on earth. Some are striplings in terms of millenniums. At least one of them—Mount Erebus near the northwestern edge of the Ross Sea—is a living mountain exhaling black gases, capable of deluging the ice-covered island with boiling lava. It is the best-known evidence that the heart of Antarctica still is beating.

Many of these mountains now are rising from graves of ice. Perhaps fewer than a million years ago the frozen ocean which now covers the interior of the continent was hundreds of feet deeper than at present, and buried peaks which now rise high out of its white desolation. Life seeks out their sunlit summits now. Heavy frosts and winds sculpture their ice-free sides; their deep valleys are a haunted blueness. Both for adventure and for scientific exploration they offer rich rewards, and as more is known about them more problems arise.

Somewhere in the Antarctic Continent are the "lost Andes," the missing arc in the ring of ancient mountains encircling the Pacific Ocean and one of geology's greatest mysteries. For countless millenniums some titanic force has pushed out of the Pacific in all directions, piling and folding the rocks in front of it into mountain ranges, often with abysmal depths at their bases. Links in the practically continuous chain are the Aleutian Islands, the mountains of Alaska and the Rockies, the Windward and Leeward islands in the Caribbean Sea (which actually form part of the Pacific chain although in the Atlantic), the Andes, the volcanic highlands of New Zealand, the high islands of Melanesia rising out of great ocean depths, Formosa, and Japan. All these mountains are of similar geological structure, great sheets of rock formed mostly on ocean bottoms and folded over one another like layers of cloth.

The Andes continue to the southern tip of South America. The island of South Georgia and the Orkney Islands are basically of the same structure—they constitute a fishhook-like curve in the chain. This chain continues into Palmer Land, the northernmost part of the Antarctic Continent, almost directly south of Cape Horn. The ranges bordering the west coast of the Ross Sea however have many affinities with the ranges of New Zealand.

From the Palmer Peninsula the Andes are "lost"; whether they turn westward or eastward cannot be determined. This leaves a break in the chain half the width of a continent. If the break can be filled in with ranges of the same folded structure, with some continuity between them, the "Pacific ring" will be considered proven. This in turn would give substance to significant deductions on the structure of the crust of the earth itself and the mysterious forces which have produced its wrinkled contour. The nature of the great Pacific thrust is as yet unknown—it appears still to be in progress. Some hold that more than a billion years ago the moon was torn out of the present Pacific basin and that the earth has been adjusting itself to this terrible wound ever since.

One such link may be Antarctica's "dead mountains"— the Edsel Fords, discovered from the air by Admiral Byrd in December, 1929. These low, pyramidal peaks cover about ten thousand square miles along the 145th meridian at the northeastern corner of the Ross Sea, and are constituted by four parallel ranges separated by blue glaciers which empty into the shelf ice.

These are mountains that were born dead, were buried, and now have been exhumed. They are built up of layer after layer of sedimentary rocks—slates and sandstones— folded over each other. The rocks, approximately fifteen thousand feet in thickness, are old ocean bottom; they are the compressed, petrified erosion of a continent, swept into the sea by floods, rivers, and winds over millions of years. These folded strata are believed to represent the greatest accumulation of such deposits anywhere in the world. The greater part of this erosion probably took place when Antarctica was essentially free of ice, since the structure of the rocks indicates strongly that the original sediment from which they are formed was carried by water. Such an accumulation calls for an immensely long period of tepid peace in the life of the rampaging earth.

But this continental debris was poured into a lifeless abyss. The oceans all over the earth have teemed with life since the first crablike trilobites crawled through the offshore ooze a half-billion years ago. At no time have the Antarctic waters been sterile of life. Wherever marine animals or plants with shells or bones exist they leave their signatures in fossils as the mud of their graves turns to stone.

Yet the folded rocks of the Edsel Fords, so far as it has been possible to examine them, are free of any evidences of life during the period when they were laid down. It is difficult for a paleontologist to imagine a lifeless ocean, as this paucity would seem to indicate. Lack of geological dates written in fossils also makes it impossible to determine the period of the sedimentation or to reconstruct anything of its history. Did it take place before life began?

The folded structure, however, is very similar to that of the Palmer Peninsula mountains, whose rocks teem with evidences of ancient life and which are identified as extensions of the Andes. The structure is similar also to that of the Queen Maud ranges south of the Ross Sea, giving rise to the possible hypothesis that the jumble of peaks is an eastward extension of these mountains.

In the Edsel Fords, as in most of the mountains forming part of the Pacific ring, there is evidence of much past volcanic activity and of great sheets of hot rock which rose to the surface from the depths of the earth. These are the so-called "plutonic invasions" of the sedimentary rock. One of the unsolved mysteries of the range is the presence of large deposits of "black quartz," the dark color of which may indicate that it was buried for millenniums under the earth where it was not exposed to weathering.

In the not-too-distant geological past the Edsel Fords were completely buried under the continental ice. The sheet over this part of the continent retreated and now reaches the shelf only in large glaciers flowing slowly down shallow valleys; this results in terribly crevassed areas, making the region of the dead mountains virtually inaccessible by ship or land. It is covered now with "highland ice"—a comparatively thin but continuous ice blanket generally conforming to the contour of the land upon which it lies. There are, however, many rock outcroppings above this ice, all showing evidence that glaciers once flowed far above the present snow line.

Southwest of the Edsel Ford ranges and nearly continuous with them, occupying much of the Edward VII Peninsula which is the southwesternmost extension of Marie Byrd Land, is an entirely different and equally curious group of mountains. These are the Rockefellers, also discovered by Byrd early in 1929. They have no structural relationship to the Edsel Fords nor, for that matter, to anything else in Antarctica. The group consists of about a score of low-lying peaks and ridges almost completely smothered in snow, some of which appear only as bulges in an otherwise level white surface. Altitudes range from about five hundred to two thousand feet. Where rock surfaces are exposed above the névé they are curiously pink, of the type of pink granite used for tombstones. None of the rocks of this group, of which granites are by far the most abundant, are sedimentary.

These hills, in the opinion of Dr. Laurence M. Gould of the University of Michigan, geologist of the first Byrd expedition, may be granite blocks carved out by erosion of less resistant materials around them. The land level below them has an elevation of only about three hundred feet, and it is quite possible that if all the ice melted the Rockefellers would be found to constitute a small archipelago in quiet waters. No evidence has been found that there was ever any volcanic activity in this particular region.

During the summer months there is considerable melting of névé in the Rockefellers. This crystallizes again as "blue ice," in contrast to the white ice formed by compression of the sandlike snow. The snow around the bases of the hills becomes quite slushy during the warmer season, with the result that the range is interspersed with blue ice fields, some of which extend from seven to ten miles into the valleys. Gould reports "curious circular patches of darker ice, caused by rocks burying themselves through absorbed heat during the summer months, which give to these fields a freckled appearance. A real lake about three miles in diameter, which at the time of our visit was frozen into solid blue ice, had been formed on the southern side of the mountains, evidently from the accumulation of melted water from the higher slopes."

On the pink granite exposures brown lichens and patches of green moss are gaining a foothold—on one such surface more than forty species of lichens were found. Brown skua gulls and white snow petrels, the Antarctic's most abundant birds, seek sheltered spots among the hills. The Rockefellers may be on their way to becoming an "oasis."

Back of the Roosevelt and Bellingshausen seas, apparently filling most of the gap between the Edsel Fords and the Palmer Peninsula, is a crazy-quilt confusion of mountains: east-west and north-south ranges, patternless groups, isolated peaks. There are the tabular, ice-inundated Walter Horlicks, the newly discovered X-rays, the far inland Sentinels discovered by Lincoln Ellsworth on his cross-continental flight. The chaotic array appears to extend a quarter of the way between the seas and the pole. Although there still are long voids on the map, the essential continuity of these wild ice highlands was made nearly certain by the flights of the Navy's expedition's eastern group, commanded by Captain George Dufek, one of the most enthusiastic and able present-day explorers. Range follows range in seemingly purposeless pattern. At least seven hitherto unmapped conglomerations of snow-covered peaks were seen and photographed, some of them only in the far distance, where it was impossible to get information as to their structure or inter-relations.

The discoveries lend support to the hypothesis that the mountains of Palmer Land twist and zigzag without any major break to the Queen Mauds and hence connect with the ranges west of the Ross Sea—that the new-found groups are the "lost Andes." Such an argument, however, is based only on apparent continuity and is open to serious question until geologists actually can get into the mountains with their hammers, find out what they are made of, and obtain information about their basic structure. It is quite possible that the real extension of the Andes turns eastward from the base of Palmer Land and skirts part of the coast of the Weddell Sea before turning across the continent. Some of the discoveries of the Navy expedition flyers, ranges apparently contiguous with the Queen Mauds curving southeastward instead of northeastward, also substantiate this belief. It might well be the case if Antarctica is in reality a dual continent split on a line between these two great seas. The country, largely because of its mountainous nature, is one of the most difficult on earth to enter with sleds or tractors and years may pass before a satisfactory answer is provided.

One of the greatest mountain systems on earth is that of the Queen Mauds with its northwestward extensions along the eastern coast of Victoria Land—the Prince Olafs, the Fishers, the James Duncans, the Watson Escarpment, the Dominions, the Darwins, the Queen Alexandras, the Britannias, the Commonwealths, the Admiralties. These mountains dwarf Alps or Appalachians; they rest on top of each other and beside each other in inextricable confusion, folded and twisted and broken. Lava which hardened to rock in the unrecorded darkness lies over rocks formed from the ooze of beaches alive with trilobites a half-billion years ago.

The Queen Mauds themselves tower in a great concave arc facing northward along the southern edge of the Ross Shelf. Viewed from the north they present a vast, tumbled array of low-lying hills around the ice beaches, increasing progressively in height to the southward where their southern slopes merge with the plateau. About fifteen miles inland stand great tabular mountain masses, reaching altitudes of nearly three miles. The foothills are black, run through with veins of quartz and granite. Their crests are ice-eroded; at some time they were buried in flowing glaciers.

The high tabular mountains present precipitous fronts to the north; even in outline, they probably always have protruded above the ice. They are composed mainly of granite, but with occasional great domes of sandstone laid down in sea bottoms standing among them. The upper reaches of many of them are horizontal beds of sandstone which must have been folded over the underlying granite in great crustal upheavals. This sandstone often is more than seven thousand feet in thickness, representing hundreds of millions of years of the earth's history. The layers are ribbed with low-grade coal, most of it dating from the mysterious Permocarboniferous geological age, somewhat more than 200 million years ago, when Antarctica presumably was covered with forests and central Africa was under an ice sheet.

The Queen Mauds have been too little explored for geologists to have resolved any satisfactory pattern out of their confusion. They are apparently almost lifeless. Only thin patches of gray lichens have been found on rock surfaces with northern exposure, only occasional skuas fly over their valleys. There is a possibility, although remote, of dormant volcanoes among them.

The Queen Mauds proper end at the Beardmore glacier on the west, along approximately the 170th east meridian. Continuing northward and marking the western coast of the Ross Shelf and Sea to Cape Adare, a wilderness of even mightier mountains towers amidst torrents of glaciers. These are probably of the same general structure as the southern Alps of New Zealand's South Island, split off in the ancient explosion of Gondwanaland. The most characteristic of the sedimentary rocks is the so-called Beacon sandstone, a chaotic conglomerate of minerals in which coal strata frequently are found. Almost identical rocks are prominent in the Queen Mauds, leading to the assumption that the two mountain systems belong to the same general earth-building complex of the Pacific ring.

The mountains of the western coast were virtually unexplored before planes of the Navy's 1946–47 expedition, led by Commander William N. Hawkes, flew over them. Commander Hawkes claimed the discovery of literally hundreds of new mountains and some entirely new ranges on some of the most picturesque flights ever recorded.

These ice-covered heights, forming the Commonwealth, Queen Alexandra, Britannia, and Prince Albert ranges, constitute one of the most impressive mountain systems on earth, comparable to the Andes or the Himalayas. They have been known since Sir James Clark Ross sailed past Cape Adare a century ago, into the ice-covered sea that bears his name. Ross and the English explorers who followed him saw these ranges from a distance and from below. They designated the positions on maps, not always very accurately, and gave the names of friends and patrons to the more conspicuous peaks such as three-mile-high Mount Kirkpatrick, Mount Harmsworth which towers 9,600 feet over the shelf ice, sharp-peaked Mount McClintock, and Mount Albert Markham with an elevation of 10,400 feet.

The Navy flights over these mountains were made between February 14 and February 20. The entire mountain system was found to be about seventy-five miles wide, cut by parallel north and south valleys, with the peaks declining in height to the westward until they merged with the ice of the plateau. Often it was impossible to get enough elevation in the rarefied atmosphere to fly over the crests, so the planes took perilous roundabout routes, flying mile after mile through serrated canyon walls of mountains and into deep valleys.

Summits towered hundreds of feet above them. Sometimes the mountainsides were stratified with vari-colored rocks—pinks, browns, purples and black—creating an appearance similar to that of the Grand Canyon of the Colorado, but on a vastly greater scale. Other mountains were completely ice-covered, while still others were gigantic masses of bare rock with few traces of snowfalls. Rock massifs rising a thousand feet above the clouds may be bare while neighbors only a few hundred feet higher are ice-sheeted, and vice-versa. Bare mountains seem to have the same orientation with respect to prevailing winds as those which are covered with ice, for peaks of these strangely contrasting types may stand within a few miles of each other, with size apparently not a determining factor.

Thick clouds often gathered around the mountains and only through occasional holes could the plane crews look into the world of mystery below. Then they saw blue and grass-green lakes of ice in deep valleys, suffused with strange blue light. One of the valleys, Hawkes estimated, covered more than ten square miles. It was surrounded on all sides by walls of brown rock about a thousand feet high, over which a half-dozen glaciers hung suspended in mid-air. The effect was like so many Niagaras frozen in space. The valley floor appeared to be covered with hillocks of loosely piled rocks and gravel, presumably old glacial deposits. This region was free of fog, which ordinarily results from a subterranean source of heat.

Hawkes spotted and photographed a dozen or more smaller valleys. On the floors of several of them were ice-covered lakes of a strange purplish-green color—a shade none of the crew had seen before. Most of the lakes were quite small, but Hawkes estimated that one of them might be as much as three miles long. A plane might land on the ice, but otherwise the country is completely inaccessible.

These lake-filled valleys were found among relatively low mountains through whose passes high winds sweep almost constantly, keeping the floors free of snow so that no ice sheet is built up. Absorption and radiation of heat by the rocks causes the edges of the hanging glaciers to melt so that there is a fairly steady flow of water down the mountainsides. Thus, over centuries, the lakes are created; some of them may be extremely deep.

Presumably such valleys are lifeless, except for the possible presence of algae in the waters. They are so isolated that it is difficult to believe any living thing could have found its way to them.

On Ross Island, just off the coast, rises the 13,200-foot-high snow-covered, three-cratered dome of Mount Erebus, the continent's only known active volcano. It appears to be approaching a period of renewed activity, for clouds of black smoke pour constantly from its craters. Hawkes had planned to fly directly over the largest of these craters to photograph its interior. This proved impossible, however, because of the smoke, and the commander contented himself with flying alongside the summit.

A mountain range with peaks rising to thirteen thousand feet, branching southeast from the eastern end of the Queen Mauds, was discovered on a flight piloted by Lieutenant George H. Anderson which approached within about 150 miles of the pole. This chain of ice-covered peaks rose above the clouds and towered far above the altitude of the plane.

Proceeding southeastward from the Bay of Whales, Anderson found a saddle-shaped depression through the coastal mountains, filled with round-topped hills whose average elevation was estimated at six thousand feet above sea level—sufficient height, apparently, to prevent any glacier from taking this road out of the continent. The depression appeared to constitute a break between the Queen Mauds and the somewhat evanescent Walter Horlick ranges.

Once out of this saddle Anderson was forced higher and higher, to the limit of the plane's capacity. The pilot described the largest of the peaks which rose before him as "looking like an enormous vanilla ice cream cone." The general direction of this unmapped range seemed to be toward the pole, which may force some revision of the current concept of the plateau as an approximately level plain of ice. These mountains may even form part of the main chain of the Queen Mauds themselves, and an interesting hypothesis is that they extend all the way to the Weddell Sea, thus cutting off about one-third of the continent. Anderson was forced to turn back when his crew members complained of "seeing pink," a warning of the dreaded unconsciousness that comes from lack of oxygen. They had been flying for more than three hours without oxygen equipment at an altitude of nearly three miles.

The southernmost mountains on earth, with the possible exception of the range found by Anderson, are the Gilbert Grosvenors, southeast of the Beardmore glacier, discovered by Admiral Byrd on his first flight to the pole. It was claimed at the time that they might be only an extension of the Dominions, but on his most recent flight Byrd confirmed his belief that they are a distinct system.

Another new complex of mountains was sighted by Navy flyers under the command of the veteran polar explorer, Captain George H. Dufek. This group had been ordered to map the coast of the newly discovered Franklin D. Roosevelt Sea, the waters enclosed by a gentle curve in the shoreline of the Sea of Bellingshausen west of the Thurston Peninsula. This sea was first observed on Admiral Byrd's 1940–41 expedition. The ice is so thick that no ship ever has been able to penetrate it, but from planes there had been distant views of a high mountain range, some of whose peaks reached an estimated altitude of seven thousand feet, and also of areas of open water south of the pack.

Within a few days after starting their operations in 1947, Captain Dufek's flyers made one of the outstanding discoveries of the expedition. This was an ice-walled, open-water bay, about square in shape, covering nearly 25,000 square miles and extending about two hundred miles into what had formerly been considered the continental coast.

The bay is an inland extension of the Roosevelt Sea, breaking for about 125 miles from east to west into a seventy-foot-high wall of ice. From what could be observed, the sea ice ended abruptly just north of the mouth of this bay. If the pack to the north could be penetrated this would form the finest harbor in Antarctica, and one of the finest in the world.

Both eastern and western shores were lined by double ranges of high mountains separated by deep valleys. One of the ranges sighted on the western shore was undoubtedly the Walter Kohlers, which Admiral Byrd named in 1941 after the brother of a former Wisconsin governor. Due to an unfortunate misinterpretation of Byrd's report these mountains were represented on the official map as running east and west along the southern shore of the Roosevelt Sea instead of north and south along the western shore. Their charted position was covered by the new-found sea. The other range of high peaks running parallel with these was named tentatively the X-ray range, a name derived from the code in which they were described in official dispatches. The highest peak was named Mount X-ray.

At the northwestern extremity of the Roosevelt Sea towered what had hitherto been represented as a lone peak, Mount Ruth Siple, named for the wife of the chief of the expedition's scientific staff, the noted American geographer who was with Admiral Byrd on all four of his expeditions. It was discovered on a flight from the Bay of Whales in 1941. This mountain now appears to mark the seaward end of one of the ranges which loom above the ice walls west of the bay.

Rivers of Ice

Ice-embalmed snowstorms of geological ages come back eventually to the warm oceans from which the sun took them in the days of flying reptiles. These creeping rivers are the Antarctic glaciers, monstrous and tortured, of inexorable, irresistible power. They spill in frozen cataracts through nearly every crack in the rim of mountains upon whose southern slopes presses the great icecap that covers the two-mile-high continent. They flow at various speeds, from inches to feet a day, depending on the steepness of the ground underneath, the narrowness of their channels, and the contour of the particular part of the high land from which they come.

This ice will continue to flow until the continent is bare rock again, for movement is an inevitable character of ice piled up over land. It melts under pressure. Thus the bottom of an ice mass is less rigid than the top, and cracks and slides in the direction of least resistance. Presumably there is a thin film of water under a flowing glacier, serving as a sort of lubricant for the groove through which the ice moves.

Antarctic glaciation now appears to be in a relatively quiet phase. Within the past few million years the continental ice sheet has been much thicker and flowed over the tops of mountains in the rim of the bowl—mountains which now protrude several hundred feet above the snow surface. Their sharp peaks were planed to plateaus by the moving ice and on their sides are deep scratches where the frozen rivers crawled past. At some distant time the mountain wall may have been nearly continuous, with the present passes cut by the glaciers themselves through relatively soft rock.

Over most of the world, particularly in the Northern Hemisphere, glaciers appear to be retreating as the present ice age, at its crest about twenty thousand years ago when much of the northern United States was ice-covered, draws slowly to its close. Even in relatively temperate regions such as Alaska, however, the decline is not easily observed. Some years there is retreat, some years advance, and the general trend can be observed only over decades. In Antarctica we know that glaciation was more extensive in some distant past than it is at present, but whether this fact reveals the trend to a more or a less temperate climate cannot be determined. Certainly the temperature has not reached a point where there is any appreciable summer melting. A major decrease in the ice, however, probably would come with a slight temperature decline, which would mean less annual snowfall and consequently less building up of pressure.

In the Antarctic, as elsewhere, there are living and dead glaciers. The latter are found in narrow, nearly level valleys extending seaward from the bases of ice-covered mountains. Ice rivers which at one time reached to the ocean now come to abrupt stops at various points in their channels and leave bare rock, washed by trickling brooklets in summer, for the rest of the distance to the shore. Such glaciers cannot advance any farther, partly because of decreasing pressure behind them and partly, it is possible, because of the melting of their edges in warmer summers. These are, however, isolated phenomena in the south polar regions and no general conclusions can be drawn from them. Only if measurable retreats could be observed for twenty or more years would they offer telling evidence that glaciation for that particular part of the Antarctic Continent was in a temporary decline. There is no way of discerning change in any of the larger glaciers; summer and winter they continue to pour their billions of tons of ice into the seas, as, presumably, they have been doing for at least ten million years.

Some of the Antarctic ice rivers are by far the largest on earth, and among the most majestic spectacles. These are the glaciers which flow into the Ross Shelf through breaks in the Queen Maud Mountains—usually the turbulent confluences of many ice streams discharged from the continental shelf and slithering like white snakes through whatever interstices they can find. They constitute rough, steep, high roads leading to the plateau; always they are flanked by majestic mountains with multi-colored walls whose peaks reach into the clouds.

The mouths of these glaciers are about forty miles apart along the southern edge of the shelf. There is the Liv, to the eastward of the international dateline, through whose walls Admiral Byrd passed on his first flight to the South

Pole. It is about seven miles wide and extends through the mountains for forty miles, joined during its course by eight or ten smaller tributaries.

Next in line to the east is one of the most impressive of these frozen rivers, the Axel Heiberg, Amundsen's "great glacier," crossed by the discoverer of the South Pole in December, 1911. It is not likely anyone will try to cross it again; about every feature of this high, rough road the Norwegian used the word "devil."

He approached it, after traversing the Ross Shelf from the Bay of Whales, across rough undulations in the ice like waves breaking against a seashore. Most of the way his dog-drawn sledges moved slowly through low gray fog or blinding snow. Nearly everywhere he found the blue ice crevassed and broken, especially where the glacier was compressed between great mountains, such as snow-covered, gabled Mount Don Pedro Christophersen and Mount Fridtjof Nansen, both reaching altitudes of more than thirteen thousand feet. The party passed under the shadows of Mount Nilsen, down whose precipitate sides bright and shining cataracts of ice plunged wildly, and Mount Hanssen whose round top "is covered by an extraordinary ice sheet so broken and disturbed that blocks of ice bristled in every direction like the quills of a porcupine. They glittered and burned in the sunlight."

Amundsen's group came to one place where the "ice was so ground and broken that there was positively no place where one could set foot. It looked as if a battle had been fought there with blocks of ice for ammunition. They lay pellmell, on top of the other, in all directions and evoked a spectacle of violent confusion."

This region Amundsen called the "Devil's Battlefield." Through it, he said, it was necessary to travel ten yards from side to side to advance one yard. At one place a broad chasm was bridged by a rib of ice barely wide enough for a single sled. On each side yawned fearsome chasms. "It was," said the explorer, "like walking on a tightrope over Niagara."

The party then passed through the "Devil's Gate." Straight across the glacier was a ridge about twenty feet high, in the middle of which a six-foot-wide fissure had opened. It was possible to squeeze the dog sleds through and the party emerged on the plateau across the "Devil's Ballroom." This appeared at first like a large lake of blue ice but it was, they soon found, double-floored. When they walked across it there was a "sound like that of walking on empty barrels." For square miles a foot of air space separated a thin upper crust of smooth ice and a badly crevassed surface underneath; when one of the sleds broke through, its runner came to rest on the edge of one of these crevasses of unfathomable depth.

Of all the Antarctic glaciers, the Axel Heiberg is notable for the roughness of its channel. In about the middle of its twenty-seven-mile course it reaches an altitude of slightly more than eleven thousand feet, then descends very steeply for about 2,500 feet. Amundsen's drivers had difficulty keeping their sleds under control as they descended this precipitate slope. The prospect was discouraging because they realized that they would have to climb the same height again before reaching the plateau. They actually emerged at an elevation of 10,920 feet, probably having chosen the most difficult of all the ice roads into the continent.

In quick succession to the eastward two more great ice rivers, the Kent Cooper, named for the president of the Associated Press, and the Isaiah Bowman, named for the late president of Johns Hopkins University, empty into the Ross Shelf. Then, running in a straight line almost due southward for about ninety miles, comes the Thorne glacier which veterans of the various Byrd expeditions believe might provide the easiest, although one of the longest, approaches to the plateau. Fifteen miles wide at its mouth, it narrows to about five miles at the point where it emerges from the continental ice sheet. It is relatively smooth and, with its tributaries, constitutes an extensive river system. Its eastern wall is a series of isolated, flat-topped mountains. This glacier may well have been a great coastal river with forested banks in the days when Antarctica was free of ice. At its southern portal stands ten-thousand-foot-high Mount Weaver in whose rocks have been found not only extensive coal beds but fossil tree sections eighteen inches in diameter. This is undoubtedly one of the most inviting parts of Antarctica for geological exploration.

Antarctica's best known, and perhaps largest, ice river is the Beardmore, which extends for more than a hundred miles between two black, pink and purple mountain ranges from the southern end of the Ross Shelf to the plateau. This glacier, from ten to twenty miles wide, rises from an elevation of about two hundred feet at its mouth to more than seven thousand feet at the point where it joins the ice sheet covering the continent.

The Beardmore was discovered and traversed by Sir Ernest Shackleton on his first attempt to reach the pole in December, 1908. Three years later it was the road chosen by Scott for his tragic journey.

A turbulent and terrible blue river is this glacier, with its surface of hard, continental ice broken by hundred-foot-high frozen Niagaras, with mile after mile of tumbled ridges and crevasses along its sides where it is joined by other ice rivers. It looks like a frozen Hell. Perhaps nowhere else on earth does man feel so ephemeral in the face of eternity, as all who have trudged and crawled up this mountain-walled creeping torrent can testify.

The Beardmore is like a valley on Saturn or Jupiter. On the west rise the Queen Alexandra Mountains, completely ice-covered, with rounded summits towering to elevations of two miles. Through their high passes flow a half-dozen other blue rivers from the plateau of Victoria Land, some of them plunging hundreds of feet down straight walls of rock and creating a turbulence of frothy ice such as would result if the waters at the foot of Niagara suddenly were frozen. Loftiest of the Queen Alexandra peaks is Mount Kirkpatrick, a tower of white ice 14,600 feet high; even more conspicuous is the Cloud-maker, nearly three miles high, which stands about half-way between the shelf and the plateau. Through this white wilderness of mountains the high winds from the great emptiness of the continent sweep in hurricane gusts.

Not quite so high, but even more rugged, are the Commonwealth Mountains which wall the Beardmore on the east. Nearly all these peaks also are blue-helmeted with ice. At the head of the glacier near its western wall is one of Antarctica's strangest mountain groups, three eight-thousand-foot-high peaks standing side by side, of which Mount Buckley is the most prominent. This is composed of perpendicular cliffs of sandstone containing six seams of brown coal, each about eight feet thick. Southeastward from the head of the glacier is still another range of ten-thousand-foot-high mountains, the Dominions, which long were believed to be the southernmost on earth. Challenging this distinction is the Gilbert Grosvenor range, about a hundred miles to the eastward, discovered by Admiral Byrd.

Two Navy missions flew down the Beardmore on their way off the continent. They found the source of this mighty torrent in a merger of two streams which flow together out of the plateau. Between them is a remarkable natural feature—a flat, almost ice-free area of about five square miles protruding more than a thousand feet above the snow—which may be the top of a low mountain whose peak has been planed off by flowing ice. The glacier itself, the aerial photos show, falls quite abruptly for about three thousand feet between two walls of high mountains upon whose sides are stratified belts of dark maroon and rust-red. After that the decline is quite gradual until the great ice river flows into the Ross Shelf through relatively low foothills.

Travel along the sides of the Beardmore is highly perilous, but it is sometimes necessary because of the long stretches of crevassed ice. With the roar of doomsday great avalanches of ice and rock plunge down the mountainsides and roll across the glacier, crushing everything in their path.

Showers of dust from avalanches are responsible for one curious feature reported by Sir Ernest Shackleton—mud-holes in the ice. Sometimes considerable areas are found peppered with pits full of brown mud and covered with quite thin coats of ice. This mud gradually sinks, presumably to the bottom, and boulders often are found three or four feet below the surface.

One of the most interesting of the great valley glaciers that empty into the Ross Shelf is the Wade, between whose vertical walls of black and brown mountains, twelve miles apart, flew the two Navy planes on Admiral Byrd's second flight to the South Pole. Near the western bank they detected what looked like a wriggling brown snake—a sinuous, ice-free area about three hundred feet wide and fifty miles long filled with piles of reddish-brown rocks.

On another flight Major Robert Wier discovered what is probably the largest known glacier in the world, a distinction formerly accorded the Beardmore. This ice river, which breaks through the Queen Mauds near the eastern edge of the Ross Sea, is shaped curiously like an hourglass. It is fifteen miles wide at its mouth, narrows to only two or three miles about fifteen miles inland from the coast, and then broadens again as it approaches the plateau. As it emerges from the continental ice it widens to thirty miles, with an extremely steep gradient of about seven thousand feet in sixty miles. This glacier is shadowed on the west by a continuous line of ten-thousand-foot-high mountains.

On the east are lower peaks from four to five thousand feet high. The plane flew alongside the western range, so that the mountain walls seemed just outside the windows. Major Wier went through this glacier about 3 A.M. late in February, with an exceptionally bright sun rising over the western horizon. When the plane hit a certain spot in relation to the light the ice-free mountainsides glittered with unearthly colors. The predominant shade was a curious purple, similar to that of a purple grackle's feathers. Entire mountains appeared like single great scintillating gems.

Wier described the surface of the glacier as "like a silver washboard." However, he did not see any of the frozen cataracts that are characteristic of most of the ice rivers that flow through the Queen Mauds. No tributary streams were observed flowing in at the sides. As a result no badly crevassed areas appeared—an important consideration for anybody seeking a tractor road to the plateau.

Another enormous glacier was sighted by Commander William M. Hawkes flowing out of the Commonwealth Mountains on the western side of the Ross Shelf. This presumably is the same great ice river whose mouth was observed by Sir Ernest Shackleton on his first attempt to reach the pole. He described it as extending northwestward as far as eye could see between walls of sharp-peaked mountains. Shackleton was able to penetrate the glacier for only a few miles. Hawkes, because of cloud cover, was unable to locate the outlet, but looked down on the glacier in all its wild, chaotic grandeur as it emerged from the ice ocean of the plateau.

Three ice streams, creeping around black crests of low

mountains, flow together to form this great frozen river. Where they meet they create a region of crevasses and pressure ridges which rise to heights of a hundred feet or more. It is like the meeting place of three swift mountain rivers. As the glacier flows downward toward the shelf it is joined by other tributaries, each in turn producing pressure-ridge areas. The surface is comparable to a titanic rollercoaster with a succession of ice cataracts several hundred feet high.

A cosmic white octopus is this icecap covering more than five million square miles at the bottom of the world and the glaciers are its tentacles which coil with irresistible strength around low mountains and islands. Once free of their narrow channels through the high ranges they tend to flatten out and flow together over the low piedmont and shallow inshore waters. Thus, it is believed, are formed the great ice shelves like the Ross. This whole ice plain of more than two hundred thousand square miles might be considered as an island-dotted sea "captured" by the continental sheet.

A quite different picture is presented on the shores of the continent directly south of Australia where the coastal mountain ranges are relative dwarfs, hardly as lofty as the Appalachians. Here nothing stops the expansion of the polar icecap along its entire front. The glaciers discovered to date along the shores of Wilkes and Enderby lands have been comparatively small local streams of ice formed in the valleys of the coastal hills themselves. A somewhat similar, although more chaotic, pattern of glaciation is that of the Palmer Peninsula. Here there are unnumbered glaciers, but they are not tentacles of the continental sheet; they drain only the high hollows of the southward extensions of the Andes which cover this northernmost arm of Antarctica.

A glacial pattern similar to that of the Queen Mauds probably exists on the Weddell Sea side, south of Africa. The region has been little explored, even from the air, but the discovery of ice streams as large as the Thorne or the Beardmore would not be surprising. The gradients, however, are not likely to be as extreme since the mountain ranges, although forming an almost continuous wall, do not reach comparable altitudes. Such, at least, was the impression of the German expedition which surveyed by plane a considerable segment of this coast just before the last war; they recorded and photographed dozens of relatively small frozen rivers flowing into the Weddell Shelf. The flyers also saw many "dead glaciers" in the mountains, streams of ice which may once have been mighty torrents but which have receded to the point where they no longer can get past barriers of hills in their paths.

All the Antarctic islands also are glaciated. The frozen streams, while usually quite small, may prove of considerable significance as barometers of the decline of the Antarctic ice age, if such actually is underway. Their sources are highland lakes of ice whose increases and decreases can be measured from year to year much more easily than can those of an ocean of ice in the sub-stratosphere so great that any fluctuations it may undergo are unobservable.

Oases in Ice

Somewhere on the Antarctic Continent there may be an isolated region, perhaps steam-heated by hot springs or with a furnace of molten lava under the earth, where the ice sheet has been unable to establish itself. There, it is conceivable, some of the completely unknown life of two thousand millenniums ago may have persisted to the present. Fiction has been written around the fantasy of ancient man in some such warm island—but the Antarctic Continent has been ice-covered since long before the earliest pre-human appeared on earth.

Islands of life in the Arctic icecap are well known. In northern Ellesmere Island, the explorer Greely reported a grassy valley among ice cliffs where musk oxen browsed. But this is life of the present, of which very little exists in Antarctica; any animals or plants in an Antarctic island must necessarily be survivals from a very distant past.

One day in late February, 1947, there was flashed to the *Mount Olympus*, Admiral Byrd's flagship, an exciting message from Captain E. E. Bond, commander of the western task force which was surveying the continental coast. One of his pilots, Lieutenant Commander Bunger, had sighted the Antarctic explorer's dream—an enormous area entirely free of ice. The news naturally excited great interest in the outside world and aroused wild speculation.

Bunger and his crew were flying inland across the Knox Coast over a flat, featureless terrain of ice, when they suddenly found themselves above a strange valley about twenty miles square. Open water lakes were spread like emeralds and amethysts among chaotically heaped piles of reddish-brown rocks. The valley was free of ice and névé but was enclosed on three sides by towering ice walls. It was open toward the sea and lay approximately five miles inland. The plane's instruments showed an elevation of about two hundred feet above sea level.

Three of the lakes were from one to three miles long, and there were about ten smaller lakes. The colors of the waters were brilliant, ranging through greens and blues, in the bright sunshine of the Antarctic summer. In one of the smaller lakes reddish streaks spread like spokes of a cartwheel from a small, red island in the center.

A few days later Bunger returned and made a landing on one of the larger lakes—an extraordinarily bold exploit since he had no means of knowing the depth of the water or the danger of striking barely submerged rocks. Landing and takeoff, however, were without incident. Members of the crew dragged their hands through the water and found it "not uncomfortably cold." The air temperature was 36 Fahrenheit. Beside the lake, under a glittering wall of ice, was a sloping, rocky beach. Probably, Bunger reported, it would make an excellent camp site.

The valley appeared almost lifeless; no birds, plants, or fish were seen. It is highly probable that closer examination of the rocks would have revealed lichens and mosses, for these grow in far less hospitable areas. The waters, however, contained algae of at least three varieties—blue, blue-green, and red—which account for the different colors of the lakes. These one-celled plants are among the most primitive forms of life extant on earth. They range through an evolutionary scale, with the red species regarded as the highest, presumably representing millions of generations of progress from the blue-green forms which constitute much of the scum on stagnant waters the world over.

This area might be regarded as a scene out of the earliest or the last days of life on earth—when living things first were establishing themselves in the waters or when, with the inexorably approaching ice death of the planet, only the simplest and most adaptable of organisms will be able to survive.

Several hypotheses were advanced when the discovery first was announced. One suggested that the region overlaid a so-called batholith, a mass of hot rock buried several miles deep after slowly pushing its way upward from beneath the earth's crust; prevented by pressure from melting into lava, and finding a vent through the surface, it becomes a volcano. Yellowstone National Park is the top of such a formation. A rock mass of this sort might act like a hot-air furnace in the basement, with a constant flow of heat upward which prevents the building up of an icecap.

Another hypothesis was that of "radiant heating." It is conceivable for a small area in Antarctica to be so oriented with respect to prevailing winds that snow is swept away as soon as it falls. The surrounding ice then tends to focus the sun's rays on the bare rocks, which have a considerable capacity for absorbing heat; a great deal of this is collected through the three months of summer sunshine and slowly re-radiated.

It was not until the next summer that the mystery was partially solved when a landing party from the Navy icebreaker *Burton Island* camped for a week in the oasis. They found that it was a marginal moraine left by a retreating glacier which, as it receded, dropped great masses of gravel and boulders picked up somewhere in the interior of the continent. There is considerable evidence that glaciers in this part of the continent are receding, or have retreated in the recent past.

The actual forming of the "oasis" may have occurred many years ago. Any recent advances of the ice did not have sufficient push behind them to surmount the hills of rock which had been piled up, for the glacier had barred its own road. The ice rivers of this region flow very sluggishly compared with the torrential glaciers to the eastward which, surmounting every obstacle, pour into the Ross Sea. As a consequence any returning ice has flowed around the area, pouring into the sea in two arms and building up a thick ice shelf which has the deceptive appearance of land, and which it would be impossible for a ship to penetrate.

Early reports, it appeared, were somewhat in error, due to the appearance of the shelf. Actually, although the oasis had been described as being several miles inland, it is on the edge of the sea and its elevation hardly rises above sea level.

Water in the lakes first was reported as fresh, but samples showed that it ranged from the salt content of sea water to mild brackishness. The lakes appear to be of two sorts. The larger ones are arms of the sea coming up under the ice shelf; the smaller are ponds formed by melting glacier ice, which, finding no outlet, gradually grows saltier. One of the major problems of the men who camped there was to obtain fresh water for drinking; snow, which is very rare in the oasis, had to be melted.

The region itself, the Navy scientists found, was a wilderness of rock piles strewn in the utmost confusion. Stones dropped by the retreating glacier were of all sizes from that of a boulder to a large pebble. Among them black and red garnets were abundant, but none of the stones were of gem quality.

The profusion of colors among the rocks was such as to provide an almost perfect natural camouflage. A helicopter from the icebreaker returned to take off the party after a week. The men laboriously had cleared a landing space, surrounded it with bright yellow flags, and set up a white tent. Yet the pilot, hovering overhead, had great difficulty in spotting them. They finally attracted his attention by flashing a signal mirror in his eyes.

A few weeks after the discovery of the Bunger oasis, at the start of the Antarctic autumn with its cold and returning darkness, another ice-free area of much the same sort was discovered near the foot of the Vestfold Mountains more than five hundred miles to the westward. A succession of green lakes, like a string of emeralds, was strung for about twenty miles along the continental coast. The area was estimated roughly as close to a hundred square miles.

Most of the lakes were green, but a few seemed red and one was black. Another was dark green in the center, shading to blue near the banks. The plane flew low enough to observe that these bodies of water were covered with thin new ice—certainly they had been unfrozen a few days before. They were separated, as in the first oasis, by brown and reddish hills of jumbled rocks, some of which were two hundred feet high. The pilots observed two long, fairly straight black lines, which from the air looked like two-lane tarred highways stretching between the lakes. These were presumed to be the lines of old lava flows.

Quite near this second oasis, giving further support to the underground heating theory, was discovered a great open-water bay, about ninety miles wide and extending about seventy miles into the assumed coastline, in which a naval fleet easily could find shelter.

Before these two discoveries the best-known ice-free region in the Antarctic was Dry Valley, near the old British base at McMurdo Sound. This is the bed left by a retreating glacier, about two miles wide and extending inland for seventeen miles between high, snow-covered cliffs to an oval lake at the foot of an ice wall. Members of Scott's first expedition spent a summer week in this majestic valley which, like the oases found by the Americans, at present is apparently lifeless—Scott's men were unable to find even any traces of fossils in its rocks. Dry Valley presents one of the most impressive scenes of desolation on earth. The floor is strewn with blocks of black stone, some of them as much as twelve feet in diameter; piles of glacial debris, mostly fine gravel, rise in forty-foot-high cones. The edge of the great glacier at the head of the valley is a nearly vertical, glittering wall about forty feet high. During the summer months streams flow from the glacier, feeding the lake.

Only one vernal valley was found by members of Admiral Byrd's 1941 expedition. This was on Lagotellerie Island off the west coast of the Palmer Peninsula—a green hollow about an acre in extent, surrounded on all sides by ice and snow fields. The canyon floor was completely covered with green moss and lichens; in some places the moss was quite thick, forming a moist, springy carpet under the feet. The expedition's botanist found one variety of grass and one small, unidentified flowering plant. This probably represents the southern limit of higher plant life.

The Ross Sea

The area in the Antarctic best known to explorers is the Ross Sea and Ice Shelf. Almost directly south of New Zealand, it covers about a quarter of a million square miles and cuts deeply into the continent to within fewer than seven hundred miles of the pole. It is approximately bisected by the 180th meridian, the international dateline where today becomes tomorrow.

Ships enter this sea through a picket fence of icebergs. To the horizon, lining wide, black boulevards of ocean, stretch these weirdly carved ice goliaths. Small ones rise a hundred feet above the water and cover a square mile in area; others are estimated to occupy a surface area of more than a hundred square miles. Winds, sun, and waves have carved these bergs into shapes of palaces, cathedrals, pagodas, mosques, ships, dinosaurs, statues of men and of angels. Two floated side by side, not more than five miles apart, while the ships of the U. S. Navy's 1946-47 expedition were making their rendezvous on New Year's Eve at the edge of the ice. One seemed a close model, on a gigantic scale, of the Capitol at Washington, built of white marble inset with emeralds and amethysts. The other was twice as large, with the shape and proportions of the White House. This probably is an impressionistic description, for likenesses often are created in one's own imagination, yet each of the ten or more naval officers on the bridge of the expedition's flagship gave essentially the same description. There was less agreement about a sky-blue ghost ship with grass-green sails and a titanic statue of George Washington against the horizon, as described by some observers.

The ice cathedrals and palaces are weird blends of white, greens, and blues. The blue is a shade not seen elsewhere on earth; it is a shining blue, bluer than the bluest summer sky or than Georgian Bay on an early autumn evening. Next to white, it is the predominant color of the Antarctic. It appears wherever there is a rift in the pack ice, and in the domed roofs of caverns hewn by waves into the interior of icebergs—caverns so enormous that a battleship could easily sail into one of them. Being in one of these caverns is like being in a dead city on some other planet. Everywhere is absolute silence, the cumulative silence of a million years. The surface of the water surrounding the bergs is glass-smooth.

Amidst the bergs one coal-black mass protrudes from the water. This is Scott Island, the only speck of land within five hundred miles in any direction. It is stern, menacing, unapproachable. No one has succeeded in scaling the icy, hundred-foot cliffs which rise from the sea on all sides.

The Ross Sea is covered with a blanket of ice three to

ten feet thick. This is the frozen surface of the ocean, which forms every winter and tends to break up in the summer. In early January, the Antarctic midsummer, it should be "rotten," like the ice of a New England lake in mid-March. But the pack is ribbed with ridges of a quite different kind of ice, fifteen to twenty feet thick, some of them as much as five miles wide and thirty miles long. These ridges are chunks of the great ice shelf that rings much of the Antarctic Continent; they break off in late summer, and slowly drifting northward, are marooned by the south polar autumn, and frozen into the new-forming sea pack itself. This ice is like steel. It is hard and amethyst-blue. It is solid, the result of millions of tons of pressure in the continental icecap for many years; it does not easily "rot." Against such a barrier the ordinary ship is helpless—only a tough icebreaker can smash a lane of open water through, picking weak spots wherever possible, at a speed of one or two miles an hour.

Scattered through the pack are lanes and lakes of open water, some of the latter covering as much as a hundred square miles. Four Navy ships were marooned in one of these, and for seventy-two hours the attending icebreaker, the Coast Guard's *Northwind,* tried vainly to cut a way out.

Meantime the shores were closing in on the ships. The lake was growing smaller, the bergs drifting closer and closer. Finally, just in time to save some of the craft from serious damage, a southward breakthrough was made. Only then was it discovered that the ships and narrowing lake together had moved eighteen miles farther north without any perceptible motion—by the time the escape was completed the lake had almost entirely disappeared. The *Northwind* and its charges crashed five miles southward through slushy ice where they entered another large body of open water which had not existed a few hours before. It was about as large as the earlier lake on the first day they sailed into it and it was uncannily familiar. Essentially it was the same lake, with much the same shore contour and the same white ice islands located in the same places. In other words, the lake itself seemed to have moved ahead of the ships. The flotilla, by moving five miles south, was in the same spot it had left and thirteen miles north of where it had stopped three days before.

Had the lake jumped over, or dived under, a wall of ice five miles across? Obviously neither. What had actually happened seemed hardly less extraordinary, although physicists aboard were able to give an explanation. Pressure of wind against the ice had carried the lake northward and, with it, the motionless ships. At the same time an approximately equal amount of pressure had been released behind. As the first lake closed and disappeared another area of open water, with a very similar pattern, had been created.

This is a sea of frozen tempests, which in the ocean of ice parallel wild winter storms in the North Atlantic. The pack is driven in front of the wind with such force that nothing can stand in its way. It flows around, or climbs over, any obstacle. Icebergs, floating majestically and leisurely a few hours before somewhere beyond the horizon, like ocean liners cruising in a summer sea, are caught in the drift and move wildly in every direction—sometimes with the pack and sometimes, their enormous under-water structures immersed in powerful ocean currents, against it.

Sometimes little motion is perceptible in such a frozen tempest. It is too slow for observation, seldom exceeding two or three miles an hour; there is no observable ridg-ing of the surface of the ice. When open-water lanes are cut their surfaces are waveless, and little wind is felt on deck.

At other times, however, something like a naval battle with the deafening roar of artillery fire rakes the scene. Such a spectacle was described by Dr. Alfred Ritscher, commander of the German Antarctic expedition of 1938-39, in his confidential report to Adolf Hitler:

The smaller pieces of ice were driven forward by the wind, usually in the opposite direction to the ocean currents. But since the large icebergs with their tremendous expanses under water are de-pendent only upon the ocean currents, they broke with great force through pieces of ice which were coming toward them. They caught up with and passed one another at different speeds, determined by their various sizes, crossing in front of one an-other and crashing together with loud noises. Every-thing crashed and thundered in a wild battle. . . .

The pack ice extends several hundred miles southward from Scott Island. Ships break through it into iceberg-filled open water, a part of the ring which nearly encircles the continent. Before them looms a wall of ice, from fifty to a hundred feet high and five hundred miles long; it is unscalable and impassable. The glittering white cliffs, ramparts looming over the cold waters, provide one of this planet's most awesome spectacles.

A dozen mighty glaciers, pouring through interstices of the Queen Maud Mountains, fill the landlocked southern half of the Ross Sea with a shelf of floating ice from two to nine hundred feet thick and covering about 200,000 square miles. This mass is pushed from behind by all the pressure of the billions of tons which cover the polar plateau.

There is one major obstruction—Roosevelt Island. This snow-covered, saddle-backed 3,600 square miles, rising a thousand feet above the level of the shelf, is the largest body of land in the Ross Sea; it is the wedge that splits the ice. One part of it is turned eastward around the island. This becomes the Ross Shelf, which covers about 120,000 square miles. The other is turned northwestward—this is the thirty-thousand-square-mile Prestrud Shelf.

Between these two, and owing its existence to the wedged division, is a little indentation of open water or thin ice in the face of the looming green walls—the Bay of Whales, Antarctica's best-known and most secure harbor, the base of five major south polar expeditions. Normally it is in the form of a triangle with its apex touching the northern shore of Roosevelt Island; this was approximately the case when Sir James Clark Ross first sailed into the bay in 1842. He entered a natural harbor large enough to hold and hide a battle fleet, about ten miles wide and extending for ten miles into the ice shelf.

The sea wall of the shelf was encountered about ten miles north of the present edge. When the white wall was surveyed by Scott in 1902 it had shifted southward about thirty-five miles from the position reported by Ross, or better than a half-mile a year. Since then it has been advancing northward again at a rate of about six feet a day. These movements presumably reflect the ebbs and surges of the great ocean of ice which covers the continent's interior across the rim of mountains.

Amundsen in 1911-12 found a harbor of about the same size reported by Ross and established his base camp, Framheim, on its western shore. The next camp established there was by Admiral Byrd on his first expedition. This first Little America was set up at the end of a small arm of the bay, Ver-sur Mer Inlet, named for the Brittany village where the Admiral had landed on his trans-Atlantic flight. Since then three other Little Americas have been located in the same general neighborhood.

Once around Roosevelt Island, the two shelves tend to coalesce again. One mass of about sixty trillion tons and another of twenty trillion tons move inexorably toward each other across the narrow bay of open water filled with floating icecakes at a speed of three or four feet a day. Every few decades the two masses crash, with about the most stupendous manifestation of force on earth. A great chunk is cracked from one or the other—which mass suffers depends on internal stresses at the time—and floats northward as an iceberg, or several icebergs. When this happens, the temporarily closed Bay of Whales is re-created, with the size of the indentation at any given time depending on the size of the chunk and the time that has elapsed since the crash.

The two shelves apparently have been creeping toward each other for nearly a half-century. The first expedition led by Admiral Byrd in 1928 found the bay only five miles wide. It was thought at first that Amundsen's report of sixteen years earlier had been in error, but every succeeding expedition has found the gap in the ice shelf still narrower. In 1947, when U. S. Navy ships skirted the towering walls of the barrier seeking the entrance, there was no assurance that a safe harbor existed. Calculations had indicated that a collision might have taken place in the last four or five years, leaving only a straight, impassable high wall of ice. However, a gateway less than a half-mile wide was found in the face of the shelf and the scouting icebreaker reported that it opened into a bay about four miles deep. The expected crash apparently had occurred in the winter of 1945-46 and had evidently been a relatively easy collision—the only result was that a piece about the size of the present bay had been cracked from the Ross Shelf. Immediately the two shelves again began creeping toward each other across the gap, so another crash will occur in a few years, and sooner or later the Bay of Whales will be closed for a decade or more. This will mean the loss of the only good harbor in the Ross Sea where ships can approach close to the continent and remain in calm water. It never will disappear permanently, of course, because the process must repeat itself at least once every half-century.

The shelf itself is reached from the Bay of Whales by climbing a 45-degree, hundred-foot slope. This is a hard

half-mile walk over the fine, sandlike snow that covers
the ice; usually it has a thin crust through which boots
crush at every step, while sharp south winds lash the face.
The narrow terrain of bay ice below the shelf, over which
all supplies must be hauled, is subjected to enormous pressures exerted in different directions. As a result it is piled
and distorted into great fields of pressure ridges—fantastic blue mountains and twisting valleys within whose
dazzling mazes the wanderer may get hopelessly lost in
a few minutes. Within the valleys, from whose sides open
mysterious grottos, there is a perpetual blue twilight during the three months of summer.

The shelf itself is not, strictly speaking, a part of the
Antarctic Continent although its hills, slopes, and valleys
have all the appearance of snow-covered land. It is a
world made of ice, the largest of three great sheets of
anchored, floating ice in Antarctica's major embayments.
Another, less than half the size, is found in the Weddell
Sea, south of Africa; still another is the Shackleton Shelf,
covering a total area of about twenty-five thousand square
miles, which is located a thousand miles west of Little
America. Similar formations have been built up all over
the world during the recurring ice ages—such a shelf, in
fact, once covered most of the North Sea and similar, but
much smaller, floating ice sheets lay over the Baltic and
Irish seas. They result from tongues of great glaciers
which project from the land into sheltered, relatively
quiet waters, where they become partially grounded on
the bottom or upon rocks and islands. This must be in
an area free of strong ocean currents which would break
off the floating projections. These tongues are built up by

the accretions of snow each winter; over the course of centuries they grow and coalesce into a single ice sheet which remains relatively stable for perhaps millions of years. The forward growth of such a shelf is stopped by sea currents—all three of Antarctica's great shelves end abruptly against a belt of open water which lies south of the pack ice. This is a result of the circum-polar current in the Antarctic Ocean which appears to flow completely around the continent. Extensions of the shelf beyond this belt are snapped off and shot northward as icebergs.

Although more scientific experiments and surveys have been carried out on the Ross Shelf than anywhere else in Antarctica, the basic phenomena of this ice world remain little understood. Generally, it is assumed, the most important factor in maintaining the shelf is the accretion of snow each winter which approximately balances the melting of the original glacier ice. Ice near the edge of the barrier also is built up by crystal formation, just as frost forms on a windowpane in winter. Winds blowing in from the sea lose most of their moisture in the first few miles and this moisture congeals as ice crystals, adding layer after layer to the thickness of the shelf.

Curiously, the deeper one drills in the ice the higher the temperature becomes. At a depth of sixty-five feet it is 10 degrees below zero Fahrenheit through the year. At 135 feet below the surface it is minus 8 degrees; the heat of the water below rises slowly through the crystal structure. This rising of water heat through the ice, by the way, lately has been found to be a factor of some importance in the weather of the Northern Hemisphere. Partly because of it the temperature of the Arctic basin is slightly higher

than that of surrounding lands—notably northern Siberia
—and hence not so favorable a place for the accumulation
of the great masses of cold air which finally spill over and
descend over North America and Europe as storm-bring-
ing "highs." Thus the birthplace of much of this continent's weather is on the other side of the North Pole.

Thunder rolls across the white waste of Antarctica as if
over a midsummer sky. These rumbles are caused by a
curious phenomenon of the shelf investigated by Dr.
Thomas Poulter, seismologist of Admiral Byrd's 1939
expedition. To begin with, water solidifies in crystals.
Thus the structure of ice is made up of crystals of various
sizes—the larger the crystal, the easier it is for water vapor
in the atmosphere to condense upon it, causing it to grow
still larger. And there is a great deal of moisture-laden air
in the Ross Shelf.

Dr. Poulter chopped a hole six feet deep in an ice cake.
When he held his bare hands two feet above the top of
this hole he could feel the air blowing upward. The fact
that air circulates within an ice hole means that the larger
crystals grow even at considerable depths—and as crystal
size increases the physical strength of the ice structure decreases. A layer several feet thick frequently becomes so
unstable that it cannot support the weight above it, and a
relatively minor disturbance may cause a considerable area
to collapse. The surface may settle a barely perceptible
amount, or it may fall an inch or more. Collapse of even
a relatively small area will produce a loud report, like a
rifle shot; this is known as a "snow tremor." One of large
magnitude may spread for miles in all directions with a

thunder-like rumble. This is an icequake, comparable in every respect except size to an earthquake. One such tremor was heard for twenty minutes at a distance of at least fifteen miles from its starting point.

There are tides as well as winds in the ice. One of the Byrd expeditions reported a recurrent tilting of the shelf at Little America over a period of twenty-four hours; it was in proper harmony with the moon for a tidal effect. These tides cause an elaborate system of cracks in the barrier, apparent only in the form of shallow, parallel depressions in the surface. Dr. Poulter found evidence of a three-foot tide under the shelf near the Bay of Whales. The gravitational pull of the moon is hardly sufficient to raise observable tides in the plastic ice itself, but the weak crystal structure is ridged in frozen waves by the constant harmonic agitation of the water below.

The shelf ice for some distance from the sea's edge, Poulter's investigations showed, is composed almost entirely of compacted névé. Snow piles up year after year on the ancient ice from the plateau which flows downward in the great glacial rivers. Eventually this continental ice, pushed deeper and deeper into the water by the accumulating weight, melts; the ice formed in situ takes its place.

This shelf ice builds up quite rapidly. Between 1941 and 1947, for example, the third of Admiral Byrd's Little Americas was completely covered. Veterans to whom the camp had been home for a winter night shoveled and sawed through four feet of compacted névé to enter through a hatch in the barracks roof. They slid down into the darkness and a temperature of about one degree above zero. Above ground level was a perfect Antarctic summer day, only about 10 degrees below freezing.

Flashlights showed walls and roof tapestried with thin sheets of ice crystals in fantastic designs. These walls had been bare when the men left them. The crystal formation still was in progress and presumably will continue as long as any moisture seeps into the buried rooms. At one place the roof had been ripped at a point where two buildings had joined. The result was a skylight of ice and névé four feet thick through which shone a dim purple light. The same phenomenon was reported later by scientists who dug a deep cellar in the ice under their tent for measurements of the speed of sound.

The cold was dead—the sort of cold that could be experienced nowhere else but under ice in utter blackness where the air has been imprisoned and no living thing has been for years. It was a stagnant pocket of cold, black cold instead of the sun-filled, wind-filled, blue-and-white cold of the world above.

Although about a dozen exploring parties—including those of Amundsen, Scott, and Shackleton on their dashes toward the pole—have traversed the shelf in various directions, the greater part of it remains a region of mystery. Everyone who ventures into the white darkness, blizzards, and mirages returns with tales of new natural wonders in this world of ice. Even more than the continent itself, it is like the surface of another planet. It is lifeless everywhere, except for occasional skua gulls leisurely winging overhead; there are no pockets of rock or water where even the hardiest and most primitive of living things can establish a foothold.

Exploration of this lifeless waste is perilous, for large sections of the ice are gridirons of invisible crevasses, often more than fifty feet wide and running in roughly parallel lines. They have been traversed, up to the present, only by dog teams led by men cautiously feeling their way ahead on foot. Perhaps the most notorious of these crevassed regions cuts across much of the shelf at about 81 south latitude and constitutes what appears to be an impassable barrier for any tractor party attempting to reach the mouths of the great glaciers which provide broad highways into the polar plateau.

The Weddell Sea

Second of Antarctica's great seas, nearly bisected by the Greenwich meridian and facing the Ross Shelf across two thousand miles of ice-shrouded continent, is the Weddell.

It is, according to the testimony of all who have sailed through its berg-filled waters, the most treacherous and dismal region on earth. The Ross Sea is relatively peaceful, predictable, and safe.

Explorer after explorer, following the trail of the British sealer James Weddell who first entered these waters in 1822 and was driven back by winds from the pole which his ships could not buck, has ventured into the region. Few have gone as far as the shelf ice which extends outward from its shores—in fact, only within the last ten years has there been more than a dotted line on maps to delineate its coastline. In 1949, for the first time, an expedition trekked across the shelf and set up a base on the land. Above the coast tower range after range of high, ice-covered mountains.

The pack in most winters is at least twelve feet thick.

Apparently no permanent belt of open water washes over the ice cliffs of the shelf, as is the case on the other side of the continent. Over the ice most of the time lies an ocean of white mist. It is a sea of howling winds, of spectres and portents with frequent mirages, luminous purple clouds racing over the sky, and ghostly halos around the sun and pale daytime moon.

It is a sea of legends. Sailors still tell, half-believing, of the merman with long green hair which one of Weddell's sailors reported to the commander. The man made the sign of the cross on the deck and kissed it as warrant he was telling the truth. "I concluded he really must have seen what he described," the explorer—seal hunter wrote.

The Weddell Sea is notorious for its "flash freezes." Within a few hours relatively loose, soft ice will become hard and packed solid, with no advance warning. All mariners are warned in sailing directions to be on constant lookout for the start of such a freeze, for there is little chance of escape once it gets underway unless an icebreaker accompanies the exploring ship. This has meant disaster for at least three expeditions—especially that of Sir Ernest Shackleton during the first years of World War I.

The experience of Shackleton and his twenty-eight men trapped for 165 days on floating ice cakes made the Weddell Sea the scene of one of the greatest dramas of human endurance and tenacity in history. Out of the nightmare of storm and misery the figure of the leader emerges as a superman of modern times.

As a junior officer Shackleton had gone into the Antarctic with Scott in 1901. Seven years later he had traversed the continental plateau to within 100 miles of the pole. He was back in England when Scott and Amundsen made their epic journeys, attempting to finance a more ambitious expedition of his own. He proposed to land on the Weddell Shelf and proceed by foot straight across the South Pole to the Ross Sea, where a ship would await him.

For this long trek he carried sixty Eskimo dogs and several motorized vehicles built to run over snow; he was the first to consider motorized equipment in polar exploration. The expedition left England August 1, 1914 —ill-omened, for the war was starting. At the last moment Shackleton and his entire party volunteered for war service, but their offer was refused.

Even for the treacherous, unpredictable Weddell Sea this was an abnormal summer. Pack ice was met as far north as latitude 58, and only on the last day of the year did the wooden ship *Endurance* cross the Antarctic Circle. A few days later it was through the pack and sailing in a belt of open water. One day Shackleton counted five hundred giant icebergs. Then a white wall of ice one hundred feet high loomed in front of the *Endurance*. For several days the ship skirted this barrier, seeking some indentation, like the Bay of Whales on the other side of the continent, where a landing could be made.

On the night of January 18 came a "flash freeze," greatest terror of the Antarctic navigator. In a few hours loose ice was consolidated into an unbroken pack through which no progress could be made. The expedition was hopelessly trapped, more than a thousand miles from the nearest habitable land; the ship could only drift with the northward drifting ice into six months of darkness and careening icebergs. Three years before a German expedition had been caught in the same way and been carried northward for 260 days through the winter night until the ice broke with returning summer. The best that Shackleton and his men could expect was a similar fate.

Frozen tempests came with the dark. The *Endurance* was caught in mountain-high crashing billows of ice piled up by the eternal winds from the south. "The ice floes," wrote Captain Frank Worsley, skipper of the ship, "appeared to us to be alive, fighting each other, hurtling one against another, and uniting only to use their mighty forces against the *Endurance*. One day there was a terrible noise as of a thousand guns going off and before we could realize what had happened the ship was lying on her side."

The crew worked for four days and nights before they got the craft on her bottom again. Soon she began to leak badly—once everybody, including Shackleton, remained at the pumps for seventy-two hours without sleep. Day after day through the winter the battered ship disintegrated. When the sun returned it no longer was seaworthy and was almost certain to sink as soon as the melting pack left it free in a lane or lake of open water. The peril grew from hour to hour with the lengthening daylight and on October 27, 1915, Shackleton ordered the *Endurance* abandoned. This was at about latitude 69. Through the winter night the ship had been carried northward more than four hundred miles. On the whole, however, the strange voyage had not been uncomfortable; quarters had been warm and food adequate.

All the provisions were unloaded on the ice, together with fifty dogs and three whaleboats mounted on sledges. A tent camp was set up on what appeared to be the most stable part of the floe, then about six feet thick but already showing signs of breaking up as the Antarctic summer moved southward. While the last of the unloading was in progress came an omen, thus described by Worsley: "We heard a funeral dirge, measured and deliberate in its dolefulness, apparently coming from nowhere in particular. Then we saw eight emperor penguins intently regarding the ship, and making the funeral chant. They are supposed never to make any sound but a whistle. I have never before, or since, heard them make any sound similar to their sinister wailings that day."

The next day "two massive floes jammed the ship's sides and held her fast while a third tore across her stern, ripping off the rudder as though it had been made of match wood. The shock of the impact was indescribable. Great spikes of ice forced their way through her sides."

A few hours later the twenty-nine men marooned on the drifting floe watched the *Endurance* plunge under the ice.

Standing before them, Shackleton tossed his gold watch into the water and ordered the others to do the same. The appurtenances of time were a useless burden now. Then, one coin after another, he threw away a pocketful of shillings and half crowns. The King's silver could purchase only a little more weariness with its weight. Last, more reluctantly, he hurled into the sea a treasured keepsake— his gold cigarette case.

Seldom have human beings been in a more desperate plight. A raft of fragile ice which daily grew narrower and thinner was carrying them northward toward the world's stormiest seas where it was certain to disintegrate hundreds of miles from human habitation. It might break up beneath them at any moment. There was enough food for a month, allowing fourteen ounces daily for each man, but this was not of immediate concern because during the summer months penguins and seals were certain to be in the pack.

Shackleton's plan was to march across the drifting floes northwestward for about three hundred miles toward Paulet Island, an ice-free rock in the sea. There, a few years before, a Swedish expedition whose ship had been caught in the ice had spent a winter and when they were rescued had left behind a large cache of food. The party started out, the men dragging the heavy sledges which carried the whaleboats and the dogs hauling seven smaller sledges loaded with food. The pack was crisscrossed with pressure ridges through which roads had to be chopped with axes. Progress was desperately slow; in seven days a total distance of ten miles had been covered, and men and dogs were near exhaustion. Shackleton realized that the march was futile. The party could only remain where it was and drift helplessly northward with the pack, hoping against hope that it would eventually bring them somewhere near land.

Food sank near the vanishing point; all but one of the dog teams was slaughtered and eaten. Life on the pack appeared exceptionally scanty that summer but one night when the meat was nearly exhausted, Worsley relates, the camp was suddenly surrounded by thousands of Adélie penguins. For 165 days the drift continued through the Antarctic summer until, on April 9, 1916, the ice raft was disintegrating so rapidly that the party launched the three boats in a swamping sea filled with loose, drifting ice. This was at about latitude 63, a distance of 570 miles north of the point where the *Endurance* first had been trapped in the pack. Six days later the drenched men came to land— a narrow, rocky beach of Elephant Island in the South Shetlands—and a perilous landing was made.

A more inhospitable place hardly could have been found. It was completely barren of life. A few feet back of the beach rose an almost vertical black mountain wall down whose slope every few minutes crashed great boulders. Nature had turned loose her artillery on the ship- wrecked explorers. Wearily and painfully they launched the boats again and seven miles to the westward arrived at a low, sandy spit about thirty yards wide where there was safety from rock falls, some shelter from the wind and, of greater importance, a penguin rookery and a few elephant seals.

Shackleton and five companions immediately took to sea again in one of the whaleboats with the hope of reach- ing South Georgia and returning with a rescue ship for the marooned party. They finally came to the whaling sta- tion of Grystviken after landing on the wrong side of the island and trekking across its mountains. Two rescue ef- forts failed. The first, with a Norse whaling ship, was stopped by a "flash freeze"; the second, in an Uruguayan trawler, was turned back by ice in sight of Elephant Is- land. Then Shackleton secured from the Chilean govern- ment a small steel lighthouse ship which succeeded in pushing through the pack to the marooned men.

They had spent 128 days on the narrow beach, swept constantly by blizzards, when the rescue was effected on August 20, 1916. They had lived in a stone hut built of rocks which they had found buried under the snow, with the two whaleboats serving as a roof. Nearly all the time the beach had been under a pall of fog and snow; once the blizzard had hurled about ice sheets as big as window-panes and a quarter-inch thick. The experience was described by Commander Frank Wild, Shackleton's second in command who was left in charge of the party, as "an avalanche of splintered glass." Still all the men were alive and in fairly good health. They were taken back to England where most of them immediately entered the service. Half of them were killed in the next year. Shackleton dropped dead on the deck of his ship six years later when he was on his way back to the Antarctic for the fourth time; he was in his forty-ninth year. He was buried at Grystviken—the foremost explorer of his generation and, it may well be, for hardihood, courage, integrity, and imagination the greatest explorer of any generation.

Demons of Ice

Compared to the icebergs of the Antarctic seas, those which come out of the Arctic to menace the shipping of the North Atlantic are like mice alongside whales.

The bergs are the temperamental, runaway offspring of the polar cap, with the perverseness of living monsters. Green, white, and blue—they cavort and turn handsprings northward. It is an endless parade to death, for the paths they follow—the ways of the invisible deep currents— force them irresistibly into warm northern waters to their doom.

The great glaciers which flow through the mountain interstices to the sea coalesce to form the shelves—such as the Ross, the Shackleton, and the Weddell. There is constant pressure against these shelves and when they reach the point where they can build up no further, great chunks crack off and are cast into the ocean.

The breaks come without warning. Sir Douglas Mawson observed one while sailing within about three hundred yards of the edge of the Shackleton Shelf. Suddenly, a million-ton mass broke off with a loud report and disappeared in the sea. For a few moments it alternately rose and sank, all the while splitting up, until finally there were about a dozen small bergs. These presumably drifted north as far as the pack ice where they became trapped.

For the brief summers of their lives icebergs are the monarchs of their world; against them nothing can stand. But they start to age rapidly as soon as they are born. The water in which they float rises occasionally above the freezing point and the sun of the Antarctic summer beats upon them. They become waterlogged and tend to disintegrate. Great holes appear in their sides just at the water line, like blue-vaulted caverns extending for hundreds of yards into their interiors. Quite often the melting is so unbalanced that they lose their equilibrium and turn on their sides or stand on their heads. Many of them never get north of the Antarctic Circle but eventually turn into slush in the polar sea itself; some, however, may wander for ten years or more before reaching their inescapable destiny. There are enormous differences in size, ranging from dwarfs no bigger than an American city block to giants comparable with a small state.

Icebergs act as if they had brains: they sometimes chase ships with uncanny precision. When the four ships of the Navy's 1947 expedition were moored in the Bay of Whales the entrance from the Ross Sea had shrunk to about three hundred yards wide. One day a million-ton monster, moving about a mile an hour against wind and current, sailed into this gate between the ice walls and blocked it completely, almost like a cork in a bottle. It was as difficult a bit of navigation as can be imagined. For about thirty-six hours the great chunk of ice remained motionless in this position, imprisoning the little flotilla in the bay. There would have been no possible way of blasting itself loose.

Then the great iceberg started on the move again. Without grazing its sides it sailed majestically into the bay itself and came to rest against the ice shelf, in line with the ships. They cut loose from their moorings and sought safety in the open waters of the Ross Sea beyond the edge of the shelf.

For two days the iceberg remained in control of the situation. Then, as if weary of waiting on its intended victims, it sailed through the entrance again with perfect precision and eventually disappeared over the western horizon. Both its entrance and departure from the Bay of Whales were against the prevailing wind. No deep currents, which might have pushed it in the face of the wind, could be detected in the sheltered harbor.

This iceberg had projections from its sides like giant guns in firing position. Officers of the *Northwind* who had served during the war in Greenland waters recalled the German strategy of disguising a ship like a small iceberg. An expert helmsman could hardly have maneuvered a craft with greater precision than the mysterious, seemingly intelligent forces that steered this monster.

The iceberg projected about fifty feet above the water. Presumably several hundred feet were under water and in the path of some erratic ocean current of which there was no manifestation on the surface. The undersea streams are the chief propelling forces of icebergs; against the push of such a current the strongest wind provides only a feeble resistance. This phenomenon is particularly noticeable in the Ross Sea pack where, in the middle of wild storms, giant ice masses appear from unexpected directions and proceed slowly, steadily, and majestically against the wind. They plough through the thin pack ice with far greater power than any icebreaker.

About the only recourse of a ship pursued by one of these ice dreadnoughts is to run away—easy enough in open water but likely to prove extremely difficult through solid pack. In the event of a collision the thin-hulled Navy ships would have been crushed like eggshells.

The earth's most spectacular iceberg region is the open water just north of the Ross pack. During the Antarctic summer of 1946–47, a string of giants, stationed from two to ten miles apart, stretched in a five-hundred-mile fence along approximately the 70th parallel. This kept the pack ice about two months behind schedule for its summer break-up; the pack encountered in December would have been normal for late October, Antarctica's early spring.

The ice bucked by ships that year was much worse than any hitherto reported. There had been, apparently, no major weather change; temperatures were normal. However, the exceptional concentration of the big bergs along the northern face of the pack may well have prevented the escape of the floe ice northward into warmer Pacific waters. Some of the bergs may have been drifting through the pack for years before the currents arranged them in the observed picket-fence formation. There is good reason to believe that the pack will continue so long as this fifty-mile-deep line of obstructions remains essentially unbroken, for the floe ice is not blown northward by the wind with sufficient force to break it up and push it through the relatively narrow interstices of the fence.

Most common of the Antarctic giants are the tabular bergs. These are great floating mesas, cracked off from the edge of the shelf ice, which have been building up for several years through snowfall and crystallization of moisture. Such bergs have perfectly flat top surfaces, with at least the upper portion formed from stratified snow or névé which has been compressed into ice. They are relatively light, with considerable amounts of air trapped between the loosely cemented crystals. Always they are pure, lustrous white—objects of breathtaking beauty when seen in the distance. They protrude out of the water from forty to two hundred feet and range in length from a few hundred yards to more than fifty miles. One a hundred miles long and wide was seen by a Norwegian whaler off Clarence Island in the South Shetlands on January 7, 1927. He reported that its height was approximately 130 feet, which would give it a roughly calculated weight of around six billion tons—by far the world's iceberg record. The snow ice of these tabular bergs is quite easily sculptured by sun, wind, and waves so that they often take on fantastic shapes.

Among the tabular bergs float soft green and blue bergs, usually much smaller. These are "glacier icebergs," broken off from the ends of glaciers which stop abruptly at the coast and which have received no significant additions from snowfall at low levels. This type has a more irregular surface than the tabular bergs, with the tops often broken by crevasses. They are made of much harder ice and are mire resistant to weathering.

Another type, "ice island bergs," originate from ice tongues extending outward from the shelf edges into the sea and are distinguished by domed or conical summits. Stranded bergs frequently have this contour and have been mistaken for rock islands, or islands covered with ice. In certain lights any berg will appear dark in contrast to the sky, or with other ice masses in direct sunlight, and this phenomenon often has led mariners to report islands where none exist.

Curious stratified black and white bergs apparently are confined to the waters north of the Weddell Sea. Some are black and opaque on the bottom and pure white on top. The dark section is caused by mud and stones picked up by the glacier from which such an ice mass is born. Others, on which mud and stones appear to be absent, have alternate layers of white and deep, translucent green. At a distance it is difficult to distinguish between the types. In both, however, the division between the white and dark portions is a straight line, with the dark portion invariably smoothly rounded by water action. Banded bergs, containing silt bands often more than fifteen feet thick, have been observed near the South Sandwich Islands.

With more than seven-eighths of their masses below water, icebergs not infrequently become stranded in shoal areas where they pick up debris of mud and rocks. Imprisoned in one spot, they usually undergo accelerated disintegration until their bottoms are sufficiently cut away or their weights reduced to set them free. Such derelicts often show extraordinary sculpturing effects.

Most curious and ephemeral are the "blue spectres," icebergs composed entirely of compacted snow and born in areas of heavy snowfall, such as the mountain valleys of some of the Antarctic islands. They are light and at first are characterized by a woolly-white luster due to the large amounts of air trapped between the loosely packed ice grains. After a few weeks the air is largely replaced by sea water and the color changes to a soft sky-blue. The spectres have flat tops like tabular bergs, but they are sculptured more easily by sun and wave into grotesque patterns which float through the mist like blue clouds. The lifetime of one of these snow bergs is comparatively short and despite their sometimes menacing appearance they are the most harmless of the monsters.

Familiar also in Antarctic sea scenery are "bergy bits," pieces of glacier or heavy floe ice which, washed clear of snow, toss about in the sea. Their average size is about that of a small house.

Caught in cold currents north of the pack, icebergs of all kinds sometimes drift quite far northward. In the Pacific they may drift a third of the way up the coast of Chile before they finally disintegrate in the warm water. They have also been reported in large numbers between Cape Horn and the Cape of Good Hope. Between the tip of Africa and Tasmania they seldom are seen north of the 40th parallel, and they are quite rare in much-traveled southern sea lanes.

The bergs north of the pack are a constant menace to navigation. In clear weather, through the completely dust-free Antarctic atmosphere, they can be seen as much as fifty miles away, but on a "white day" their forms may merge with the milkiness of the fog and be indistinguishable within a hundred yards. When the sun is shining above the fog the first appearance is of a luminous white object, like a ghost, directly ahead of the ship; when the sun is not shining the berg appears as a monstrous dark mass with a narrow black streak at the water line. The appearance usually is much larger than reality due to the curious phenomenon of "ice blink," a white or yellowish aura which appears above them or at their sides, caused by diffusion of light in the fog.

On dark, clear nights, icebergs may be seen from a distance of one or two miles, appearing either as white or black objects. The moon may help or hinder, depending on its age and position. When sailing into the moon they are difficult to distinguish; with the moon astern, an aura is created around them, making them visible from a great distance.

Presence of bergs on a cold, quiet night is manifested by a noise like that of distant gunfire, caused by the constant breaking-off of chunks. The sound of breakers against the ice masses also can be distinguished, although iceberg waters are generally quite calm—the thickly dispersed floating mountains prevent the building up of waves. Radar and sound echo detection have often proved quite unreliable; tests on the Navy expedition sometimes succeeded in locating bergs twenty-five miles away, and yet sometimes failed when the monster was in plain sight.

Stuffed-Shirted Folk

The chief citizens of manless Antarctica are birds which look and act absurdly like men. They are, of course, emperor penguins—perhaps the most unusual form of life among today's higher animals. Unless seen at close range one cannot be sure that they are not absurdly strutting little men, between three and four feet tall and weighing up to ninety pounds, who have evolved in this ultima Thule of the planet. Survivors of a wrecked Navy airplane, painfully trekking across the ice pack, once mistook a group of these birds for a rescue party and cursed heartily when their semaphore signals were not returned.

Penguins are nature's gentle satire on humanity—the odd, bowing, speechmaking birds are a link over a vast chasm of white years between the twentieth century and the time when Antarctica was a green continent and the first precursors of man had not appeared on earth. The hypothetical man from Mars might have some such form, since living conditions on Antarctica and on the world's red neighbor in space have various elements in common. The way of the emperor penguin may be the way of the struggling last remnants of mankind as the earth grows cold in some faraway future and the human race must adjust to the change or perish.

It is at least a million years since the Antarctic Continent was a forested land, teeming with bird and mammalian life, yet even then the ancestors of the emperors were old and well-established citizens. As the ice age descended, animals of the Antarctic plains and forests migrated or became extinct, one race after another. A few flying birds and swimming mammals may have been able to escape to warmer lands, but virtually all higher forms of life perished, with the notable exception of the penguin.

The penguin could not fly; it could not swim great distances. It seemed trapped for eternity in nature's graveyard. However, it was able to do what its better endowed neighbors could not; it was able to adjust to greater and greater adversities. This hardly can be attributed to any ingenuity on the part of the bird itself—it probably blundered into survival, for, despite its deceptively human appearance, the penguin is a rather stupid creature. It belongs to an older line of descent from the dinosaurs than the familiar flying and singing birds. Closest relatives, although very distant, are the ostrich and the flightless kiwi of New Zealand, both of which are "morons." It is probable that the animals of Antarctica in its green days were all quite primitive, like the indigenous fauna of Australia at present.

Of all the penguins the most conspicuous, most primitive, and most fantastic is the emperor. For all its unconscious mimicry of man, it is one of the closest of living birds to the cold-blooded reptilian ancestry of a hundred million years ago.

It is cradled in cold, darkness, and whirlwind. The emperor hen lays and hatches her single egg on bare ice, with no shelter whatever, in the unbroken darkness of the polar winter, shielded from the seventy-mile winds only by low hummocks, with the temperature seldom above minus 50 or below minus 70 degrees Fahrenheit.

Both the egg during the time of incubation and the newly hatched chick are held in a loose fold of heavily feathered skin—somewhat like the pouch of a kangaroo—between the legs and the lower abdomen. This is probably quite comfortable, for the parent has an exceptionally high body temperature of about 103 degrees Fahrenheit. Nobody knows how many days are required to hatch an egg, but Doctor Siple believes that the major part of the incubation process may be carried out inside the mother's body and that the chick breaks through the shell within a few hours after the egg is laid. If this is true, it represents a close approach to mammalian reproduction.

Both parents take part in the arduous duty of cradling the young. Incidentally, only a skilled anatomist or another penguin can tell the difference between father and mother; the sexes approach much closer to each other than in other higher animal species. Male and female are precisely alike in size and color. No difference has been observed in their behavior—with one possible exception to be described later. All sex organs are internal except, perhaps, for one or two days a year, and the birds are strictly monogamous, for at least one year.

Nowhere else in creation does the parental instinct reach such intensity as in this dark nursery. Mother and father replace one another for brief lunch and rest periods. A rookery always is set up near a lead of open water—kept ice-free even in the dead of winter by prevailing currents and winds—where a quick snatch of fish can be had without too long an absence.

Up to four hundred birds crowd together in one rookery through the winter night. Many are chickless because of the high egg loss and infant mortality rate, and these are possessed by a maternal frenzy. Whenever a parent sets a chick down on the ice there is a wild scramble of the bereaved birds to get possession of it before the other parent can lift it into her, or his, pouch. Scores of fledglings are trampled to death in these scrambles, but this seems to make little difference. A dead chick held against the abdomen seems to satisfy the overwhelming parental love as well as a living one. If no baby bird, dead or alive, is available, a bit of rock of about the same size appears to form an adequate substitute.

Actually, life in such a rookery has been observed for an extended period only once, by a party from Scott's 1911 expedition. This group, led by the expedition surgeon-naturalist, Dr. Wilson, who later perished with the commander on the return journey from the pole, made an extremely perilous night trek over crevassed ice to find it, and nearly perished on their return journey. The rookery, probably the largest in the world, was located on Cape Crozier near McMurdo Sound, where the base camp of the Scott expedition had been set up. This general region remains the "country of the emperors." Here among the ice-covered rocks along the coast the big birds are to be found by the hundreds during the summer.

The destruction of eggs and the mortality of chicks are enormous, as is also the death rate among parents as they crouch under the lee of ice hummocks to escape the wind; often they are crushed under heavy blocks. Total loss of eggs and young in a season is estimated at 75 per cent, which means that, in order for the race to survive, the average life span of the emperor penguin must be between thirty-five and forty years.

Once past the chick stage the emperor is one of the most difficult creatures on earth to kill. Birds with crushed skulls have been known to rise and shuffle calmly away after lying a half-hour or more, supposedly dead. They seem almost immune to clubs and bullets; one will survive for hours with a needle inserted in a vital area of the brain. Dr. Siple tried to chloroform one bird. After being exposed for about thirty minutes to enough chloroform to have killed ten men the bird did not seem in the least affected, and the attempt at humane execution was abandoned. Probably it had held its breath—an ability highly developed in the race by its amphibious way of life. Attacked by a sea leopard, its fiercest enemy, the tough emperor endures terrible lacerations of breast and abdomen without succumbing. This tenacity of life is one of nature's chief provisions for the survival of the race.

Although in appearance a clumsy creature, the big penguin is well able to defend itself. Its powerful flippers, with which it strikes with equal force either forward or backward, can deliver a blow powerful enough to break a man's arm. All sailors of the expedition were warned before landing not to pick a fight with the birds; they could easily have put a man in the ship's sick bay for the rest of the voyage. With the single exception of the sea leopard, most vicious of the seal family, the emperors are more than a match for the creatures they are likely to encounter, and are apparently agile enough to avoid killer whales, most fearsome animals of the southern sea. They make sledge dogs look like fools. One day a big penguin, apparently just for the sport of it, shuffled right through a team of twelve dogs hitched to a sled as if it were running a gauntlet. It emerged unscathed, but with the wildly excited dogs in an almost inextricable tangle. So far as is known, the birds never fight among themselves, except for the scrambles in the rookery. They have had a million-year lesson that they cannot survive if they battle one another as well as the malevolent elements.

One wonders what possible chain of circumstances can have brought the emperor to such a strange way of life. Of what advantage, for example, are the winter rookeries? Science has no answer, although it has suggested possible explanations. One is that the young are offered almost complete security against natural enemies during this season. Another is that the penguin thus is saved from wasting time during the Antarctic summer, when food is plentiful, and can feast on fish and crustaceans to its heart's content with no responsibilities to interfere with the banquet. Thus it builds itself up for the ordeal of the next winter.

At best, the survival of the emperor penguin as a species is a matter of extremely delicate balance. A difference of one or two per cent in the chick survival rate, which might be brought about by a very small disturbance of the bird's way of life, would mean extinction in a generation. Perhaps, after all, it has chosen a wise course—it is still alive, while most of its contemporaries in the time scale of evolution disappeared thousands of years ago. It has found a niche in the world by clinging to the old homestead.

Neither Dr. Siple nor Jack Perkins, of the U. S. Fish and Wild Life Commission, after long observation, was able to find evidence of social organization among the emperors, other than the winter mating of one male and one female. The race as a whole seems to have reached the ultimate form of anarchy with the instinctive recognition that self advantage never really is served in the long run by taking advantage of others. It is a society which needs no law. Penguin government has passed beyond or around the communism of ants and bees, the individualism of men and tigers.

They have developed independently the human institution of the sightseeing excursion. Little groups get together and make long journeys inland, sometimes waddling leisurely and sometimes tobogganing down slopes on their bellies faster than a man can go on skis. Apparently these tourists have no purpose other than to see the country and enjoy its beauties. Sometimes they walk erect for miles, shuffling forward a few inches at a time. Around the Navy base there were wide, beaten paths over which large parties had passed; it was not difficult to speculate that the routes had been laid out by penguin tourist agencies.

Nature has provided several adaptive mechanisms which make life easier for the emperor. The pupils of its eyes have a remarkable range of expansion and contraction; they can be opened wide to enable the bird to see better in the dense darkness of the Antarctic night or close to an aperture of about two-hundredths of an inch in the intense glare of the white summer day. The feathers are not like the feathers of most other birds, supposedly modifications of the scales of reptiles and set in rows with bare spaces between. Rather, they are arranged like the hairs in the fur of a mammal, completely covering all parts of the body.

The only other member of this ancient bird race actually to inhabit the Antarctic Continent—about a dozen varieties are on outlying islands with more temperate climates and easier accessibility to fishing grounds—is an animal of quite different temperament and ways of life from the dignified emperor. This is the Adélie penguin. In appearance and behavior it is a harlequin and only about half the size of the emperor, which it outnumbers twenty to one. There is no delicate balance on which its survival depends. It is lively, mischievous, playful, saucy and—most striking characteristic of all—curious.

The Adélie, sometimes alone and sometimes in groups of four or five, is encountered soon after a ship enters the Ross Sea ice pack. The submarine U.S.S. *Sennett,* the only underwater boat ever to enter the floe, had a curious above the level of the ice. Suddenly there was a dull thud experience the first night. Its deck was about three feet on the deck; a penguin had "dived upward" over the side. There really is no other way to describe the way an Adélie comes out of the water onto an ice floe—it dives into the air.

The bird landed on its feet and looked at the curious figures who were crowding about. Then it shuffled toward Lieutenant Icenhower, the *Sennett*'s commander, and solemnly bowed. It repeated the procedure for most of the men on the deck (it did not, however, greet them strictly in order of rank, as was erroneously reported at the time). This formality concluded, the bird shuffled to a sheltered spot on the deck and remained there, speechless and motionless as a snow man, for the next two days. Then, apparently having got to where it wanted to go, it dived into the water again. This penguin is believed to be the Antarctic's first hitchhiker.

In contrast to the emperor, the Adélie mates, breeds, and hatches its young in midsummer. In mid-January the chicks start to emerge from the eggs. Courtship and mating procedures are well known from previous observations by Byrd expedition biologists. First to arrive at the rookery, sometime in late October, are the females (as with the emperors, they are indistinguishable superficially from the males). Then come the suitors, who begin to court the hens of their choice. It is a strictly utilitarian courtship and consists of gathering and fetching stones for building a nest on the ice. This is tiring labor; the average male requires from one to five minutes to gather a single pebble, depending on the distance he must travel and the difficulty he experiences pushing his way through the closely crowded females, each standing guard over the pile she has accumulated.

Once the "homes" are constructed the breeding season

starts. As described by F. M. Bryant of the Government's Fish and Wild Life Service, biologist of the 1940 Byrd expedition:

Throughout the breeding season the birds are likely to strike ecstatic attitudes on the slightest provocation. One bird usually will start the actions and the others will follow, until this behavior spreads over an entire section of the rookery. They can be compared with dogs barking at the moon.

The ecstatic attitude starts with the bird tilting its head back and stretching its neck in an apparent effort to lift the point of the bill as high as possible, as though trying to balance an imaginary ball on it, seal fashion. At the same time the flippers are waved back and forth in unison, with the stately motion of a heron in flight. Now a drumming sound is emitted from the pulsating throat, which increases in intensity and gradually changes into a gutteral ka-ka-ka-ka, reaching a crescendo and then dying away.

This usually is followed by bending the head between the legs or under a wing, and nodding it from side to side while several gruntlike sounds are uttered. There is no difference between the actions of male and female.

After the eggs are laid they are left bare for a few minutes, while the parents indulge in some more ecstatics. Females sitting on the nest never seem to eat; they will sit for sixty-five hours at a time. When light snow flakes fall, however, birds were noticed opening their beaks in a yawning attitude, presumably trying to catch some of them. In every case tested the male showed more disposition to retreat and the female to fight. When a male is on the nest with a female near by, the least disturbance brings her back and the male promptly vacates for her. Until both eggs are laid only the female sits on the nest, although the male usually is in attendance.

In connection with courtship and nest-building activities, crime and punishment make their first appearance in penguindom's utopian anarchy. Some birds seem to lack the ambition to carry pebbles a few hundred yards, one at a time, and they resort to stealing stones piled up close at hand by some more ambitious fellow citizen of the rookery. Such a thief must act with the utmost caution, for stone-stealing is a first-order thou-shalt-not—perhaps the only one yet established in penguin mores. Once a transgressor is caught, punishment is swift and certain. He is set upon by the entire community, males and females alike, and beaten with their powerful flippers. Probably he would be beaten to death were it not for the fact that almost no amount of beating can kill a penguin. Nor is there any evidence that the offender is permanently ostracized from the rookery after he has paid his debt to society.

On the other side of the ledger are nursery schools for working mothers—or fathers. Both Perkins and Siple insist on this last qualification and it should be emphasized that the terms "he" and "she" in any description of penguin behavior are used entirely for convenience. Some birds behave in a manner more attributable to females than males, but—except in the matter of egg-laying—there really is no distinction. One would suppose that the individuals who bring stones to lay at the feet of other individuals in the courtship procedure were the gentlemen of the rookery, but for all anybody really knows they may be the ladies. Or sometimes a female may court a male and sometimes a male may court a female.

In any event, the nursery school appears to be an independent Antarctic invention. Shortly after the fledglings hatch they develop ferocious appetites. The responsibility as provider of krill—a species of small crustacean—for the little household becomes far too much for one parent, and the other also must go to work if the chicks are not to go hungry. But they cannot be left alone. The fishing grounds are several hundred yards distant and in the skies hover blood-thirsty skuas, hawks of the Antarctic, whose favorite food is baby penguin. So the youngsters are herded into nurseries in groups of twenty to two hundred. On guard over each stand four or five adults, presumably birds with no chicks of their own. Fathers and mothers arrive with fresh krill every few minutes and each arrival is the signal for an uproar from the chicks.

In a few weeks after the little birds get their first feathers they are able to shift for themselves, at which time the parents abandon them and head for the open sea, where they spend the rest of the winter on floating cakes of ice. After a few weeks of wandering about in small groups, the young follow them. Food apparently is plentiful and winter is the time when the Adélie gets fat.

There are at least twenty varieties of penguins, one of which extends as far north as the Galápagos Islands west of Ecuador. All are confined to the Southern Hemisphere; those ordinarily seen in zoos are of species which have broken away from the ice hundreds of thousands of years ago and have become adapted to the ways of the outside world.

Once away from the Antarctic, an emperor's chances of survival are very small. On the ice shelf the bird lives in an almost completely aseptic atmosphere. There are no germs and there is essentially no dust, consequently the race has developed no immunity or resistance to air-borne diseases. The two females—their sex was determined by autopsy—brought back to the National Zoological Park by the Navy's 1947 expedition died within three days after reaching Washington from a fungus-caused throat malady probably contracted while the *Mount Olympus* was in Panama.

They were rather remarkable birds. When the ships tied up to the shelf at the Bay of Whales these two, perhaps drawn by curiosity, came out of the pressure hummocks and squatted on the edge of the ice. There they remained for three weeks, hardly changing position. During this time they ate nothing; they were moulting. A football field was laid out on the ice on which games were played between crews of the different ships. The birds became rabid fans—whenever a play was made which caused a demonstration among the spectators they flapped their flippers excitedly against their sides. They never offered the slightest resistance to being petted by the sailors and went along peaceably when picked up and carried aboard ship.

There at first they refused to eat, but for about two

weeks Mr. Perkins spent hours every day stuffing frozen fish, in each of which was a multiple vitamin tablet, down their throats; finally the birds started to eat of their own accord and seemed reasonably contented. Curiously enough, they did not appear to suffer greatly while the ship was passing through the intensely hot days of the tropical Pacific. Disease, not heat, is fatal to them.

Thirteen emperors brought back by the second Byrd expedition died within two weeks after reaching the United States. But three which were brought back on the 1941 expedition by Malcolm Davis, keeper of birds at the National Zoo, survived for seven years in Washington. One, probably a male, is still alive—the only specimen of its kind north of the Ross Barrier. It is kept in a refrigerated cage and all the air it breathes is filtered. Davis attributes its longevity to "luck" and to the fact that it probably had an exceptionally good constitution in the beginning.

There is a wide variation both in appearance and behavior among the different penguin species. Second only in general interest to the emperor is the king, a bird about three feet tall and weighing approximately forty pounds, which never is found south of the Island of South Georgia. It has been nearly exterminated by whalers for its oil, yet despite its unhappy experience over the past century it shows absolutely no fear of human beings. It is notable for its cry which resembles a long-drawn bugle call.

One of the best known is the gentoo penguin, a much smaller bird than either king or emperor. It is a migratory species and during the Antarctic summer comes as far south as it can find open water. Its rookeries usually are on rocky hills high above the shoreline, where it builds nests of grass, moss, seaweed, bones, feathers, and stones. A pair usually hatches two chicks in a season and its eggs, with salmon-red yolks, are edible. Its characteristic call has been described as "like a tin horn or the braying of an ass."

Flying Skulls

From the circle almost to the South Pole there is a profusion of feathered creatures whose plumage merges with
the infinite whiteness and blueness of sky and ice mountain.
These birds are the only higher forms of life, except for
a few seals near the edge of the barrier, which have been
able to establish themselves on the dead continent.

Through countless generations their bodies and their
ways of life have become adjusted to the everlasting cold
over these vast ice fields of endless days and endless
nights. Others are migrants from warmer lands—wandering fishers who somehow have found living conditions to
their liking on these dead shores. They lead hard lives in
the bitter cold, but generally the ocean affords a plentiful
food supply and evolutionary adjustments to Antarctic
conditions have been so profound that the birds have become prisoners to their harsh environment.

Antarctic birds show absolutely no fear of man. Their
behavior would provide abundant material for the in-

vestigator seeking evidence that fear is not an inborn quality but a protective reaction arising out of experience. So few men have ventured here that the living things of the ice desert have never known the threat of the most predatory of all animals.

Snow petrels, the most abundant birds of the Far South, have snow-white plumage with black eyes, bills, and feet. Only these dark parts are easily visible against a background of falling snow; otherwise bird blends perfectly with storm. The appearance is strikingly like that of midget ebony skulls suspended in air and blown by the wind. Only after eyes become adjusted to the all-enveloping whiteness can forms of birds be distinguished.

The snow petrel is by far the most common bird in the ice pack and invariably is associated with ice. Often it swarms around bergs or on the edge of heavy packs, and thus becomes of interest to navigators as an indication of conditions ahead. Snow petrels seldom are seen until the pack ice is reached, at which time they suddenly become abundant. These birds rarely go north of the Antarctic Circle and sometimes nest on the continent as much as fifty miles from the sea. They are, even more than the penguin, the most appropriate living symbol of Antarctica.

Strangest of birds met in the Antarctic is the Arctic tern—the bird of eternal day. Every year it makes a 25,000-mile flight from the dark, traveling almost from pole to pole. It is earth's greatest wanderer. The tern nests and breeds during the northern summer on rocky islands of the Arctic, not far from the North Pole, but with the first far northern sunset some impulse starts it southward over Europe and Africa, speeding through the brief intervals of darkness it encounters, to another night-less land. With late February's first Antarctic sunset it starts for the North Pole again, this time by way of South and North America. The route apparently is always the same.

All this is generally accepted by biologists. It is, how-ever, based on quite scattered observations—knowledge that the tern leaves its Arctic breeding grounds in early fall, a few dead birds picked up along the European and African coastlines in autumn and along the American coasts in spring. The northward route over the Americas and the time taken to traverse it is essentially unknown.

This slate-gray little bird with long, red bill and red feet reaches the Ross Sea ice pack about mid-December. It apparently wastes no time on its flight south, resting only for a few hours at a time to feed on fish and crusta-ceans, and moving through the skies in an almost geo-metrically straight line. It stops on the shores of Antarctic islands, since there is no food near the pole, and congre-gates in great numbers on ice-covered rocks. Although it has a wing spread of nearly two feet, it actually weighs only a few ounces, most of its bulk being made up of light feathers.

One theory is that millions of years ago its ancestors were glacier birds who followed the edges of advancing and retreating glaciers backward and forward with the changing seasons, and that the race has been unable to break the habit through the ages. It must have ice and light. About eight months of each year is spent in flight to find both together.

The migrations seldom have been witnessed because apparently the terns keep far offshore. They have, it is only fair to say, been questioned altogether. In the Far South there is a very similar bird, the Antarctic tern, which apparently never migrates northward. It is almost indistinguishable from its Arctic counterpart, but the fact remains that earth's greatest wanderer has been found at the bottom of the earth.

Earth's second greatest traveler is the wandering albatross, which circles the globe in far southern latitudes, apparently with no definite migration pattern. Sailors long believed that an albatross was attached to a ship by the sea gods as a guide and that if any harm befell it the wrath of the spirits of the deep would fall on the offending craft. Apparently the superstition, immortalized in Coleridge's *Ancient Mariner*, is as strong as ever in the American Navy. For years ornithologists have wanted to capture several albatross and place metal bands about their legs in an effort to determine their migration habits. Dead specimens also have been desired for museums. On all previous expeditions permission had been refused but in the winter of 1947, for the first time, it was granted to a representative of the Federal Fish and Wild Life Service. As soon as the news spread the crew began to grumble and henceforth every mishap was blamed on the wrath of the sea demons though actually no albatross was shot or molested. The unfortunate biologist, however, suffered a broken leg and was unable to carry out his plans; his misfortune was blamed on his defiance of the albatross legend.

One of these birds will follow a ship for days, presumably living on the garbage cast overboard. When an albatross leaves a ship to which it has attached itself it is clear indication that land is near, although none may be recorded on maps.

The wandering albatross is one of the two largest of sea birds, and among the largest of all flying birds. It has a wing spread of from ten to twelve feet and can fly easily at a speed of about sixty miles an hour. With a good wind behind, it may attain as much as a hundred miles an hour. The color varies with age, sex, and season. Sometimes the male is almost pure white—nature's way of concealment in the intense summer light over the ice pack. Females, however, never lose a small patch of black or brown plumage on the crown of the head and usually the wings are tipped with brown.

As soon as a person steps on the ice he is surrounded by flocks of brownish-black birds slightly larger than ordinary pigeons. They glide slowly, gracefully, and fearlessly around the head of the visitor; they gather curiously in the snow at his feet and peck gently at his boots. The scene is similar to that of pigeons gathering around a stroller in a city park, except that these birds are much tamer. They do not take flight at the approach of a newcomer, or at an unexpected movement. One can walk through a flock of them on the ice without starting any disturbance. They have gentle eyes and downy heads, like newborn chickens.

It is difficult to imagine a creature which appears more exemplary of innocence, despite the hooked bill, black, webbed feet, and long, sharp claws. But appearances are deceptive. This is the south polar skua, one of the most vicious and voracious birds on earth. It is the scavenger of the Antarctic and especially the scourge of penguins upon whose rookeries it preys. It has the most southerly range of any living creature in the world. One was observed by Scott within 150 miles of the South Pole, apparently flying across the continent, and others often have been seen a hundred miles inland.

These birds are fierce and bloodthirsty. They prey upon all sick or wounded creatures, and are cannibals; one killed at the Bay of Whales and left on the ice was almost completely devoured by its fellows in a few hours. A dead seal attracts great hordes of them; they peck out the eyes and rip open the skin to get at the thick layer of blubber underneath. They will pick up any strange object they see, especially a red trail flag. Like other Antarctic creatures skuas have no fear of men because they have no familiarity with them; they seem even tamer than other birds of the ice fields because they are bolder and have probably never known a dangerous enemy. They are believed to winter in the ice pack, breed on all suitable shores of the continent and its surrounding islands, and occasionally to venture north of the circle.

Bird of ill omen is the wide-winged giant fulmar, which gathers ominously in flocks like giant ravens around a ship imprisoned in the ice pack, seeming patiently to await its destruction. Next to the skua it is the most predacious—and certainly the boldest—of Antarctic birds. Its usual victims are fish, but it also preys on penguin rookeries and is reported to attack a man without hesitation, clawing viciously at his eyes. The fulmar is a heavy, uncouth bird, built like an old-fashioned airplane with a wing spread of nearly seven feet. Its structure is so clumsy that it cannot get into the air by its own efforts after a heavy meal but must spread its wings and wait for a favorable wind. It varies in predominant color from snow-white to black, but face and breast always are white.

Antarctica is the home nest of those ubiquitous birds of cold seas—stormy petrels, or Mother Carey's chickens. They are dark-brown, square-tailed little birds which breed on islands below the circle and on the shore of the Antarctic Continent. They have been observed as far as a hundred miles inland, although they are predominantly creatures of the sea, being seen in great numbers around such isolated rocks as Scott Island, at the edge of the Ross Sea. During the southern autumn many of them migrate northward beyond the Arctic Circle.

Nature is economical in moulds for life. Among the most curious of south polar birds is the whalebird, or blue belly, a highly specialized species of petrel, which has suspended from its upper jaw a fine sieve of whalebone, or baleen, through which it strains minute particles from the sea water. Thus its mouth essentially duplicates that of its Antarctic neighbor, the great blue whale, largest of living creatures. Another, and one of the smallest, members of the petrel family is the fairy prion, or Antarctic blue bird, of which a flock seen in the distance may look like a flurry of blue snow.

Leviathans of the Deep

The Ross and Weddell seas, with their palls of gray-green fog, are the habitats of the most frightful and terrible of living creatures: the killer whale, a throwback to earth's millenniums of flesh-eating dinosaurs. Schools of these flesh-hungry, malignantly smiling demons appeared around the Navy ships as they approached the Bay of Whales, as if curious about the smoke-spouting animals that had come to dispute their supremacy in these waters.

Orca gladiator, the whale swordsman, although more than three times the size of an African elephant, is a relatively small member of the Cetacea family in this part of the world. The average male is about twenty-five feet long and weighs in the neighborhood of fifteen tons; the reputedly deadlier female would probably not tip the scales at more than ten tons. Perhaps the creature's most distinctive and fearsome feature is its white teeth—ten to twelve of them, looking like small bananas about three inches long, in each jaw. With these it easily can chop a seal—or a man—in two pieces with one bite.

Streamlining camouflages the orca's great size. It is a graceful animal with snakishly slender body and pointed head, plunging through the waves like a living torpedo. The creature belongs to the dolphin family but has diverged far from the popular picture of these sea mammals—symbols of gentleness and love in early Christian art, and in Greek mythology swift messengers of Aphrodite.

The orca certainly is the only whale that would, or could, eat a man. "It will attack a human being at every opportunity," warns the Navy in its sailing directions issued for mariners entering Antarctic waters. But for all the creature's reputation there is not a single thoroughly authenticated instance of man-eating. Several such stories are found in diaries of whalers, and there is nothing inherently improbable about them, but they are not actual eyewitness accounts. All are secondhand reports of what somebody else heard somebody else describe.

Could this whale swallow a man at one gulp? There was endless discussion about wardrooms of the Jonah story as orca packs gathered about the ships, brushed against the hulls, and sent up scores of thin green waterspouts ten feet high. The consensus, after examining all authorities available, is that a very large killer might conceivably get a very small prophet down his gullet with a single gulp, but that the chances of such an event would be quite remote. Judging from the fate of seals, it is likely that a man would be disposed of in two approximately equal chunks, swallowed within less than a minute of each other.

The killer is the only cetacean—whale, porpoise, or

dolphin—with a taste for the flesh of a mammal. Most of the family are essentially as vegetarian as cows. Large ones, such as the blue whale whose favorite habitat also is in these icy waters, and which is known to reach the weight of 150 tons, are toothless. They have a sieve of horny plates—the whalebone which is used in the stays of corsets—suspended from the roof of the mouth, through which they filter the almost microscopic plant life of the seas in which they live. Mixed with it are a lot of tiny red shrimps, the "krill" which color thousands of acres of ocean blood-red. It is a tasteless diet, as all who have sampled boiled krill can testify. Such a monster requires at least a ton of fodder a day, in the form of a kind of vegetable soup. It has little time for anything but eating.

Like most giants of land or sea the baleen whale normally seems a mild-mannered, stupid, inoffensive fellow. He is slow to anger and must be made a harpoon pincushion before he becomes sufficiently irritated to fight. He has no offensive weapons and his only defenses are his enormous bulk and thick hide from which rifle bullets sometimes bounce. It is curious that in the same family and in the same part of the world nature should have placed the supreme example of the opposite economy—the beast of prey. Such certainly is the orca. He is the only enemy, except man, who can kill, or even seriously annoy, the biggest of living creatures. His only purpose is to secure his favorite delicacy, blue whale's tongue.

Two killers can dispose of a 150-ton leviathan. Each sinks his long, sharp teeth into the monster's jaw, one on each side, then together they pull his head under water. The orca can hold its breath for as long as twenty minutes, the big blue only about five. Because of this difference the deadly dolphins can keep their gigantic prey submerged until he drowns. Then they slash open his mouth and snap off his enormous tongue, letting the rest of the carcass float away untouched. Even their teeth will not penetrate the tough, inch-thick hide.

Sometimes the killers attack in packs of five or more. Two or three attend to the vulnerable jaw while the others leap on the furiously struggling monster's back as if trying to beat it to death.

Certainly no living creature can fight the orca. He is as ferocious as a tiger, forty times as big, and invulnerable to anything but weapons especially devised by man for killing him. Besides, the tiger is emotionally spasmodic in his killing; he slays, as does man, for food, for danger, or for sport. The killer slays because he has no other design for living. A hundred million years of evolution have made him an emotionless engine of destruction. He is cold death incarnate. The several thousands which frequent the Ross Sea congregate in packs of from fifty to a hundred and move in formation, with four or five swimming in a straight line with each other.

In the struggle for survival, however, other animals of polar seas and ice shelf have developed means of outmaneuvering the monster. Fast-scooting penguins can dodge the killer among the ice cakes; the momentum of his great weight puts him at the same disadvantage in chasing the light, fast birds as would handicap a mad bull chasing a fleetfooted small boy. Both the silver-white crab-eater seal and the ferocious sea leopard, nearest approach to the orca as a killer in this part of the world, actually have developed sufficient agility to roll out of his jaws from between his teeth. Nearly all adult seals captured show scars from such terrible ordeals. The first one slaughtered for food by the Navy expedition—just to vary the diet and not because of ration shortage—was an old female whose abdomen at one time had been ripped wide open. She had somehow escaped and lived to become a tasty dinner for a more dangerous animal than any whale.

Naturally the appetite of such a monster is insatiable. In the stomach of one specimen, it is recorded, were found the remains of thirteen porpoises and twenty-one seals. An entire herd of the defenseless little porpoises known as "white whales" sometimes is cornered in an ice bay by a pack of orcas and literally torn to shreds.

There can be little doubt that the killer has brains to direct his slashing teeth. He probably is the craftiest creature of the seas, if seals are excluded as essentially land animals. But fortunately for all other living things in the Antarctic he still is confined to a sea habitat, has no means of locomotion on ice or land, and can live only a few moments out of water. He may, however, have started in the direction of an amphibian existence, the first of the cetacean race to break the bonds forged by a hundred million years of ocean environment. He has reached the stage where he can stand upright in the water, stick his head far into the world above, and survey his surroundings.

There are two or three recorded instances of this. One sent a shiver up the spine of Captain Scott just before he started his ill-fated trek to the South Pole. A member of his party had ventured on thin ice with two dogs, and the group had been spotted on the water's edge by a pack of orcas. Scott recorded the incident in his diary:

> The next minute the whole floe under the man and the dogs heaved up and split into fragments. One could hear the booming noise as the whales rose under the ice and struck it with their backs. Whale after whale rose under the ice, setting it rocking fiercely. Luckily Ponting [the dog driver] kept his feet and was able to fly to security. By an extraordinary chance two splits had been made around and between the dogs, so that neither of them fell into the water. Then it was clear that the whales shared our astonishment. One after another their huge, hideous heads shot vertically into the air through the cracks they had made. As they reared them to a height of six or eight feet it was possible to see their tawny head markings, their small, glistening eyes, and their terrible array of teeth, by far the largest and most terrifying in the world. There could be no doubt that they looked up to see what was happening to Ponting and the dogs. The fact that they could display such deliberate cunning, that they were able to break ice at least two-and-a-half feet thick, and that they could act in unison was a revelation to us. It is clear that they are endowed with a singular intelligence.

At another time Tom Crean, the Scott expedition's "singing sailor," was caught adrift with five ponies on a floe which was breaking up. With killer whales raising their heads on every side, he jumped the frightened animals from ice cake to ice cake and finally got them to the safety of solid ice.

"I just kept going pretty lively, sor," he used to say in telling of his horrible experience. "Them killers warn't too healthy company."

A similar experience occurred on the second Byrd expedition at the Bay of Whales when a pack of the blotched swordsmen chased a dog team. The driver had spotted the pack at the edge of thin, rubbery ice and wisely took to his heels with his frightened, yelping animals. The whales gave chase, breaking up the ice behind the dogs with their backs. Every now and then the nightmare face of a monster, its teeth bared in a fiendish grin, would tower five or six feet out of an opening. Once the dread apparition was only about three feet away from the intended victims. The driver said later that he easily could have patted the monster on the head. All made good their escape, however. Twice small boats were chased by killer packs, Dr. Paul Siple recalls. Fortunately in each instance the ice edge was close at hand, and men can run much faster than whales can break ice under their feet.

The green, steampuff fountains blown up by the killers are characteristic of Bay of Whales scenery. Each is a whale breath exhalation. The orca, like any other cetacean, is a warm-blooded, air-breathing animal which fills its lungs normally every four or five minutes. The head remains above water only a fraction of a second, however, and just before the whale reaches the surface the air is expelled with explosive force in order to leave the lungs entirely empty, to be filled the instant mouth and nostrils are out of the water. It is this forced breathing-out that causes the fountain. The steam-like appearance is due to the condensation of exhaled breath in the cold air— precisely the same principle as that by which one sees one's own breath on a frosty day.

So far as man is concerned the great beast is not worth hunting for gain and too dangerous to hunt for sport. Bullets probably would not bother the orca unless a lucky shot hit a particularly vital spot, probably somewhere in the brain. But if a party of hunters really wanted to kill one it probably would not be too difficult. The weapon would be a harpoon strung with about four hundred feet of stout rope; to the rope would be attached two empty fifty-gallon gasoline drums. The harpoon itself would not greatly bother the animal, but the floating drums would tend to hold him above water. His strength would be taxed to the limit as he struggled to dive to the safety of abysmal depths, never quite succeeding. Eventually he would be too exhausted to continue the hopeless struggle and the hunters could approach him in a motorboat and slit his throat with a sharp knife. Such, at least, were the instructions furnished the expedition's biologists. But even their devotion to science was not sufficient to send them on orca hunts.

The Bay of Whales and the waters of the Ross Sea just outside are the particular province of the demon. Here is the homeland from which he ranges far afield but to which, judging from his numbers, he always returns with blood-dripping jaws. This foggy hole at the bottom of the world might seem a poor choice of abode for the earth's most fearsome animal, able to select any spot in all the ocean for his habitat. But for his own purposes he apparently has made a wise choice, for these are the waters of superabundant life and he has no competition in his hunting. He sticks to his lair because his hunger is so great he can satiate it nowhere else.

Hunting leviathans a century ago, when New Bedford and Nantucket whalers pursued the monsters with harpoons in open boats, was perilous and colorful. It also was highly profitable, because whale oil was essential for lighting and lubrication; then, before the days of petroleum, the sub-Antarctic was the oil field of America and Europe. Whaling is still an important business, although for Americans especially the economic urge is much less important. Before World War II it was pursued chiefly by Norwegians, British, Germans, and Japanese; only since the war have the Russians become interested.

From a picturesque, adventurous calling it long since has become a highly organized, efficient, mass-production job carried out with great factory ships—essentially floating packing plants—equipped for processing the animals into the end-products for the market as rapidly as they are killed. This has brought about an interest in preservation of the species, which soon would become extinct if there were no curbs on mechanized slaughter, for cetaceans probably are slow breeders.

The true whales of the Antarctic belong to two major groups. First, and at present of the greatest economic importance, are the whale-bone, or baleen, species, the "krill eaters," of which there are two outstanding varieties—the blue whale and the fin whale. About half the length of the blue whale, which measures from seventy to 150 feet, is taken up by the head. It is dark gray-blue in color with white spots on its belly. Its weight usually is estimated as about a ton per foot of length. The blue's closest rival in size, the fin whale, seldom exceeds ninety feet in length and is a more slender, apparently more efficient animal. It seldom ventures as far south as the ice pack.

The other family is that of the toothed whales, conspicuous by the absence of baleen in the mouth and the presence of teeth in one or both jaws. These whales travel in packs. Most of them are predacious, and polygamous in their habits; all are dangerous, although none approach the orca in ferocity.

The largest and economically most important of the second group is the sperm whale which measures up to sixty feet in length. It is a square-headed, square-jawed monster, whose head takes up about a third of its total length. It usually is coal-black in color, although old males sometimes have white heads, and even albino specimens have been reported. Moby Dick, for example, was a sperm whale. This creature is a potentially tough customer, with from twenty to twenty-five pairs of teeth in its lower jaw; however, it is not looking for a fight, will not attack a boat if unprovoked, and ordinarily will seek safety in flight. When pursued and smarting from the pin-pricks of harpoons, though, it will put up a vicious battle for life. It was with this animal that the Yankee whalers chiefly came into contact.

These Antarctic whales, given nearly a six-year respite from hunters during the war, now seem fairly numerous in the waters around the circle. Among the biologists of the Navy expedition was Dr. Raymond Gilmore of the government's Fish and Wild Life Service, whose primary

job was to take a rough cetacean census. The tanker
U.S.S. *Canisteo*, on which Dr. Gilmore was stationed,
sailed through the so-called "whale sanctuary," about
100,000 square miles in Antarctic and South Pacific waters
below latitude 40 south and between longitude 70 and
160 west, an area set aside in 1938 where no factory ships
could enter in search of baleen whales. The provisions of
the sanctuary, to which all nations with whaling interests
except Japan subscribed, lapsed in 1940, and efforts now
are underway for its renewal. In this area itself Gilmore
did not find the whales particularly numerous—in fact,
one of the reasons for its selection was that it was not considered particularly good whaling territory and consequently there was less temptation to violate it. It was intended chiefly as a refuge if the pressure on the whale
population became too great elsewhere in the Antarctic
(presumably the hard-pressed monsters would find it for
themselves). In any event, it would always contain a fairly large number of baleen families who would constitute
a nucleus of breeding stock.

The sanctuary agreement never applied to sperm
whales. They now are of relatively minor economic importance, and their extinction never would be threatened
by Antarctic whaling. Only big bulls of these species are
found in the Far South; the normal habitat is in tropical
or sub-tropical waters. These are their breeding grounds
and there are found all the cows and young. They live in
polygamous family groups, each consisting of one or two
bulls and ten to fifteen females with their calves. The
latter seldom leave the temperate zone.

The bulls in the Antarctic presumably are animals who

have been unable to find a place for themselves in harems. In some cases they are probably weaklings who have been ousted by stronger rivals. Others may be aging whales who have been driven off by stronger young bulls, for apparently the rivalry for wives, as in any polygamous society, is very intense, and males fight desperately among themseves. The slaughter of these animals by the whaling industry would not endanger the species, as would heavy sperm whaling in sub-tropical waters. The bulls of the Antarctic, however, are not numerous enough to pay for the expenses of whaling unless baleen whales were taken as well.

These latter monsters fall into a quite different category. They apparently are at least seasonally monogamous; it is possible that one bull and one cow remain together throughout their lives. They live in small family groups which migrate to the Antarctic during the southern summer and sometimes even come into the ice pack, following the vast floating red pastures of krill, the tiny crustaceans which constitute their chief food. For these whales some sort of sanctuary is essential as a refuge for breeding cows.

Gilmore was able to make some measurements of the speed of these monsters. He found that they move through the water at an average speed of from ten to twelve knots, but if frightened it is likely that they can make twenty knots, at least for a short time. This would be a good ordinary speed for a fast yacht. It is difficult to conceive of strength in a living creature sufficient to propel a hundred tons or more with such a velocity.

Gilmore conducted his census, necessarily a quite superficial one, both by sighting the animals and by picking them up many miles away with the Navy's sonar, an echo device used during the war for detecting submarines or other foreign objects under the water.

Naturally the ways of life of whales are less known than those of other warm-blooded animals because of the impossibility of observing them. They cannot be kept in captivity where they could be watched, and their natural reaction is to dive out of sight as soon as a ship approaches within observing distance, so about all that is known about them is from scattered observations of naturalists, from which it is impossible to make far-reaching deductions.

Physically, chained to an ocean habitat, they are the most divergent of mammals and, despite the horrible ability of the orca to raise its head through a hole in the ice, there is not the slightest possibility that any of the race ever can get back on land again. The seas in which the remote ancestors of the cetaceans found refuge have become the eternal prison of the race.

During the season preceding the outbreak of World War II there was a sharp drop in the catch of blue whales —more than a thousand less than in the 1937-38 season —and whale oil production dropped from about four million barrels to three million. At the same time the market price quadrupled. Japan especially increased her whaling fleet; besides oil her ships brought home nearly six thousand tons of salted and frozen meat to be sold in department stores for human consumption.

Japanese whalers were the first to return to the Antarctic after the war; two of their ships were operating just north of the Ross Sea pack during the winter of 1946-47. Not only were they in search of whale steaks but of raw material for synthetic silk, for under a Japanese process silklike fibers can be spun from whale meat unfit for human consumption. The flesh is rich in proteins and fibers are formed from it on the same patterns as are used experimentally in the United States to make fabrics from chicken feathers and the whites of eggs.

During the prewar season the first "whale transmitters" were put into use. As soon as a whale is shot the carcass is pumped full of air to keep it afloat and a lance with a flag driven into the blubber to indicate the ship to which it belongs. In clear weather the flag also enables the catcher to find the whale again, for it often is left floating about while hunting continues. If the weather is foggy the catcher may be forced to search for it for hours, and sometimes the animal is lost altogether. Under the new arrangement a small wireless transmitter is placed on the whale so that its position can be fixed with a direction-finder. The transmitter is encased in rustless steel and fastened to the lance. It transmits signals every minute, and each expedition has its own special signals.

Whether the leviathans benefited much from the suspension of hunting during the war remains to be seen; they almost certainly became more widely dispersed through Antarctic waters. Their period of grace is now most assuredly ended, for with the need of fats and oils throughout the world it is almost certain that the industry will be revived on a larger scale than ever.

Antarctic Seals

In the recent war, the United States Navy trained underwater demolition teams to blow up enemy shore defenses. These men had to be prepared to spend several hours in ice-cold water, and it was essential that they be able to move swiftly and retain free use of their hands for manipulating explosive charges. Navy scientists worked hard on the problem and after a few months of experiment devised an underwater suit which seemed satisfactory. Actually the problem had been solved by nature millions of years before by the slow experimental processes of evolution. A land animal, a close relative of the ancestors of the dog and one of the most intelligent of the developing mammals, had been turned into a sea animal— the seal. Unconsciously the Navy scientists arrived at a design quite close to that of nature: so far as it was mechanically possible, they transformed sailors into seals.

The Germans were faced with much the same problem and they solved it, although not so efficiently, in a similar manner. Once the Ludendorff Bridge at Remagen had fallen unexpectedly into the hands of the 1st American

Army it became a matter of life and death for the enemy to destroy this span across the Rhine. Swimmers in rubber suits and with oxygen apparatus which enabled them to spend long periods of time underwater were sent down the river. Most of them were killed by American sharpshooters on the bridge, but a few were captured. They could easily have been mistaken for small seals when they were pulled out of the water. The design, however, was not very efficient, for the woolen underwear underneath the suits was wringing wet with perspiration and the men were on the point of collapse from exhaustion.

American scientists, still without consciously imitating nature, did a much better job. The first real opportunity for testing the suits came when the Navy's 1947 expedition arrived in the Bay of Whales. The swimmers looked very much like particularly agile, green, two-legged seals as they lined up on the deck of the *Mount Olympus* before diving into water covered with icy slush through which floated tiny icebergs. In the water they looked like a school of young whales at play. The seal's thick coat of blubber was imitated in several layers of clothing, including two suits of woolen underwear with air spaces between, worn under the rubber suit. Black rubber flippers extended out from the feet. The suits themselves had considerable buoyancy and the sailors stayed afloat without effort. They played tag with each other among the ice cakes, turned somersaults, and flipped water at each other. These men suffered no discomfort after spending twenty minutes in the water. They were the first human beings to swim in the Antarctic Ocean voluntarily.

There was one thing the inventors could not do for

them—endow them with the agility of seals in escaping killer whales and sea leopards. Before they were allowed in the water a survey had shown none of these dangerous animals in the vicinity. Boats constantly circled the swimmers to drive away any beasts of prey that might approach. To each swimmer was attached a fifteen-foot rope, held at the other end by a sailor on a rubber life raft. The man was to be pulled in instantly at any warning that an orca was in the vicinity, or whenever his head dropped below water indicating a possible attack from beneath.

Aside from whales, five species of seal are the only mammals now found in the Antarctic and they appear, like the penguins, ideally adapted to their strange environment. They have found a niche in creation where there is plenty of food and where they have few enemies. These animals are possibly survivals from the old Antarctica, which was perhaps the ancestral land of other species of seals as well until they were driven into the water by the advancing ice.

The Antarctic seals are of no economic value whatsoever. Their flesh is fit only to feed dogs, or explorers in dire necessity; their pelts are worthless. The fur seals, vast herds of which first brought men into the southern seas, have been extinct for almost a century. They were once found in almost countless hordes on the Antarctic Islands around the Palmer Peninsula but were slaughtered indiscriminately by the hundreds of thousands—an outstanding example of human greed and ignorance. Captain James Weddell, discoverer of the sea which now bears his name, has given one of the best descriptions of this animal in his *Voyage toward the South Pole*:

The male is nearly twice the size of the female. About the middle of November the males go on shore to await the arrival of the females, who soon follow to bring forth their young. The males at this period have many battles and during the gestation of their partners are most assiduous protectors of them. The female has seldom more than one at a birth, which she suckles and rears with great affection. After the young one has been taught to swim by its mother, it is left on shore and remains there until its coat of fur and hair is fully grown. At first the young are black, but in a few weeks they become gray and immediately after acquire their full costume. Their senses of smell and hearing are acute, and their instincts are as perfect as those of the common seal of our seas.

When the islands frequented by these seals were first visited by voyagers the poor animals had not the slightest fear of man. They would lie quite still while their comrades were knocked on the head and skinned. But in a few years they became intimidated and placed themselves on rocks from which they could immediately dive into the sea. The agility of this creature is much greater than the observer would judge from its appearance. I often have seen them escape from men running fast in pursuit to kill them.

Weddell refutes the stories of sealers that the fur seals threw stones at them with their flippers. "When an animal is chased on a stony beach," he says, "it advances by drawing the hind flippers forward, thereby shortening the body and projecting itself by the tail which, when relieved by the effort of the foreflippers, throws up a quantity of stones to a distance of some yards."

In the years 1821 and 1822 no fewer than 320,000 seal pelts were taken around the South Shetland Islands alone by British and American hunters. If judgment had been used, Weddell believed, there might have been an annual catch of a hundred thousand for an indefinite period. The sealers used no discrimination. The young, left on the beaches without their mothers, perished. At least a hundred thousand were lost in this way during the fateful two years.

Nearly extinct now are the most picturesque of Antarctic seals—the sea elephant, which also is found chiefly on the beaches of the more northerly islands. It has been hunted indiscriminately for the oil from its thick coat of blubber. This is by far the largest of the southern seals—males measure up to twenty feet in length. The creature looks, as the name implies, very much like a small elephant; a clumsy and apparently rather stupid animal, it can present a fearsome appearance when engaged. A fleshy proboscis about ten inches long hangs over the mouth and becomes inflated when the animal is excited. The "trunk" serves a useful purpose quite aside from frightening enemies, however. It insures inhaled air passing over a large surface before it enters the lungs, an important provision when the temperature hovers around 50 below zero.

When a ship enters the ice pack many solitary white seals are seen on the floes. Usually they appear to be asleep; even when craft pass within a few feet of one of these animals it only raises its head drowsily and sinks back into its lethargy—seemingly contemptuous of this invasion of its floating white world. This is the crab-eater, the most conspicuous animal on the pack ice. Of its life history almost nothing is known. It spends most of its life on these drifting ice islands and only occasionally ventures on land or shelf. During the summer, however, it is fairly common near the Bay of Whales; one was found beside a crevasse nearly a mile from the water's edge. The crab-eater's food consists mainly of the small crustacea known as krill, but occasionally the beaks of small octopuses have been found in crab-eater stomachs. The stomach of one killed on the Navy expedition contained a whole octopus and a handful of gravel.

Rarest of Antarctic mammals is the green-bellied seal. This animal had not been seen for twenty years before the 1940 Byrd expedition when one was captured alive; it died, however, in a few days. The eastern group of the Navy expedition secured a single specimen in the Bellingshausen Sea. The creature has a thick, bloated neck into which the head can be almost completely withdrawn when it is attacked. It inhabits the pack ice, is rarely found more than a few feet from water, and seems to have much the same habits as the crab-eater.

These seals are sluggish in their movements on the ice and seem to have no effective means of defense. They are quite resentful of man. When disturbed they raise their heads, fill their lungs with air, and exhale suddenly with an explosive sound. Otherwise they have a high, chirping call similar to birds.

None of these seals collected to date have shown scars

due to attacks by orcas. They probably are very rapid swimmers; the short head with large folds of fat around the neck tends to make them really streamlined.

The sea leopard is the most predacious of the seal family and one of the most dangerous animals on earth; it is the scourge of ice pack and shelf. This reptile-like animal has more the appearance of a dinosaur than of a mammal. One specimen shot on the ice near the Bay of Whales for the U. S. National Museum at Washington was more than ten feet long and about five feet in girth. The sea leopard will attack a man without provocation and probably could slash off a leg or arm with its long, curved teeth. It lives chiefly on penguins, but quite often kills other seals nearly as large as itself. In striking contrast to the others, perpetually drowsy out of the water, it is always on the alert. Its movements on land appear clumsy but sailors are warned that it can probably outrun a man across the ice. It is a solitary animal and essentially nothing is known of its ways of life.

Some members of the last Byrd expedition observed a sea leopard feeding on penguins off a small rocky island. In order to secure motion pictures, several live penguins were thrown in the water. The great seal swam rapidly under water after the birds and, on reaching one of them, grabbed it by the feet and shook it violently. It had been reported that it first shakes off the skin before eating a penguin but in this case there was no evidence that the bird was skinned or that the seal did not swallow the feathers. On one occasion a dead penguin was thrown to a sea leopard swimming near the ship. The animal merely sniffed at the bird and swam away. Ordinarily penguins are captured in the water but the great seals sometimes will chase them over the ice and there is terrible slaughter when one of them invades a rookery. No sea leopard ever has been taken alive. If a pup could be found and brought back to civilization it would be one of the greatest attractions ever offered by a zoo. It is highly doubtful, however, whether an Antarctic seal could be brought back alive. They refuse to eat in captivity, even when food is forced down their throats; their lives are chained to the frozen south.

Most remarkable of the family are the Weddell seals, warm-blooded mammals that live buried under the ice all winter. A colony of approximately ten thousand of them has settled about three miles from Little America, hidden away among blue ice grottoes, marking the southernmost limit of mammal life. It is an inferno-like region of pressure ice, always suffused by a strange blue light and traversed by hidden crevasses. Here through the summer the animals live, sleeping most of the time, beside water holes in the ice through which they have access to the open waters of the Ross Sea with its bountiful supplies of fish. When these holes freeze over several inches thick they saw holes through them with their teeth. In the same way they can cut their way out when a freeze takes place while they are on hunting sorties.

In winter they live under the ice, presumably on ledges in the sides of crevasses which are covered with ice bridges. They never have been seen, but their curious birdlike chirps have been heard underfoot. Here apparently they remain through the winter night with temperatures reaching 80 below zero outside. Through the crevasses apparently they have access to the sea.

When the Navy expedition arrived at the Bay of Whales the pups were about four months old and just learning to fend for themselves. They are born in October on the surface ice of the Bay of Whales and taken back to the blue seal city as soon as their mothers have taught them to swim in shallow pools formed on the ice surface.

Men can walk among the drowsy giants—they weigh in the neighborhood of five hundred pounds—with complete impunity. The animals merely raise their heads, sometimes growl a little, and fall back to sleep. They have no fear of man because, like the penguins, they have had so little experience with him. Their presence is an important consideration in locating a base near by, and they insure some sort of food supply if an expedition should be cut off.

Spending the greater part of their lives in and around the pressure ice they are safe from killer whales. Very rarely a hungry sea leopard invades the blue grottoes in search of Weddell pups. They are completely defenseless, their movements on land are slow and awkward, and they never seem to travel very far from their exit holes. That they are generally non-migratory and that the same animals inhabit the same area from year to year is shown by the fact that three adults branded during the summer of 1934 were found six years later within a very short distance of the same spot.

Eventually, and perhaps in a very few years, the inhabitants of this frontier settlement of life on earth are doomed. The ice is constantly in slow motion and sooner or later the exits to the sea will be closed. It is highly improbable that the great seal colony will be able to make a mass migration over the ice to the edge of the bay or find another similarly crevassed area adapted to their highly specialized ways of life. They are referred to commonly as "the lost colony."

Their behavior in the stygian darkness of the winter night under the ice remains one of the mysteries of natural history. From the sounds they make they appear to be quite active and certainly are undergoing no hibernation period. Walking among these ice mountains in winter with animated seal conversation under one's feet is described as one of the strangest experiences imaginable.

What happens to these drowsy monsters when they grow old? No dead ones ever have been found. They are not cannibalistic, and skuas would only strip the flesh from the bones, leaving the skeletons on the ice. It is highly probable, of course, that once an animal loses its agility in the water it soon becomes the victim of a killer whale. But there are persistent rumors of a seal graveyard somewhere miles inland on the ice shelf to which the old animals repair when they feel the chill of coming death. The only evidence for this is that solitary animals have been seen crawling slowly and painfully over the shelf ice away from the water—evidently outcasts of the rookery and on their way to certain death. Once deprived of access to the sea they have less chance than a man of survival. It may be that some ten-million-year-old urge drives the patriarchs back to the graves of their ancestors.

Neptune's Pastures

Earth's richest pasture is the trackless two-million-square miles of ocean two miles deep which rings the Antarctic Continent.

The temperature here seldom rises more than a degree or so above freezing. More than half the area is ice-covered at least eight months each year, leaving the depths in darkness. Yet the plant growth in these frozen seas is so abundant that millions of the largest extant animals, the biggest of which require more than a ton of food a day, find abundant pasturage. Tests made during the Navy expedition showed that underwater visibility here is only about one-third as great as in the warm central Pacific. This is due almost entirely to the greater abundance of plant life. The sea flora is, for the most part, microscopic but there are countless billions of tons, presumably replete with proteins and vitamins—some of the latter very likely unknown so that Antarctic waters offer a rich field for biochemical exploration—for the great herds of whales and porpoises and the little crustaceans which color thousands of acres pinkish red.

A spoonful of Antarctic water under the microscope shows thousands of little plants, together with the minute animals which are eating them—they to be eaten in turn by shrimps and fishes which themselves become the sustenance of seals, birds, whales, and dolphins. The Antarctic is truly the well-stocked icebox of the world where food never gets stale and where the quantity never diminishes.

Here the pyramid of life is simple. The broad base is diatoms, the "grass" of the sea pastures. These are very ancient, usually almost invisibly minute, plants which have followed a unique road of evolution. The tiny bits of protoplasm, hardly larger than bacteria, apparently can move, like animals, of their own volition. Each has a shell of silica, instead of the cellulose which forms the outer covering of all other plants. They might be described as living grains of very fine sand. There are perhaps a billion of them in a glass of water from the Ross Sea. The designs of their shells are so lovely and elaborate that they have been used as models by jewelers. Diatoms multiply by division, like bacteria or protozoa, but also—supposedly under very hard conditions—they can throw off spores, like fungi, from which new family lines may arise.

Like all other plants, they are enabled to live and multiply by the basic process of photosynthesis by means of which water and carbon dioxide are formed into starches and sugars by the energy of sunlight acting on the green pigment chlorophyll, or some closely related material with similar properties. Here arises one of the major mysteries of the Antarctic. For at least six months of the year no sunlight pentrates most of the water; during the other half-year very little radiation can get through ice three or four feet thick. Navy submarine divers under large ice floes found almost total darkness. Even in ice-free water light penetration is reduced greatly because of the "soupiness"—yet the life-creating photosynthesis continues to depths of at least fifty feet below the surface.

Tests showed these waters rich—although not excessively so compared with other seas—in silica, phosphates, and nitrates needed for plant growth. This is somewhat puzzling, for the ocean receives only the debris of the Antarctic Continent; most of the water poured into it comes from melting glaciers which seldom scrape the soil. There is, though, the possibility that mineral elements in the Antarctic are brought in from equatorial seas by layers of warm water which flow under the cold continental water.

One reason for the thriving condition of the Antarctic diatoms, whose numbers appear to fluctuate little from year to year, is that no plant diseases caused by viruses or bacteria reduce their numbers. Elsewhere, in common with other living things, they are subject to devastating epidemics, but here they have found a niche in nature where only bigger things, not smaller things, prey upon them. And, of course, the possibility of an unknown Antarctic vitamin which greatly stimulates unicellular reproduction is not excluded.

Still, the fact is inescapable that all plants, with the exception of entirely parasitic groups like fungi, require sunlight for growth and reproduction—yet these microscopic plants survive through nearly six months of darkness in intense cold. The situation would seem to require that they spend the winter in a state of suspended animation—but if this is true it is difficult to understand why they have not long since been exterminated, despite their enormous number, by the billions of minute shrimp which feed on them. Do the shrimps have a hibernation period? If so, how do they survive the enormous drain on their numbers by the insatiably hungry—and countless—whales and fish? Certainly, say the oceanographers, these higher animals do not experience a season of suspended animation; whales, especially, remain very active, for they must rise to the surface of open water for air every few minutes.

Perhaps the most interesting and amazing of the diatoms are the "icebugs"—the corethrons—which live and multiply in cakes of ice, taking advantage of air and water cells between the rather loosely packed crystals. These colonies sometimes cover acres, coloring the surface of the pack yellowish-brown. Within the ice the "bugs" exist in countless billions, wearing jackets of translucent glass. They appear to be the hardiest form of life on earth and presumably will be the last to survive when the planet is covered by an ice sheet similar to that which now blankets the Antarctic.

When a chunk of this living ice is melted, filtered, and a bit of the residue placed under a microscope, there is revealed a glittering garden of moving jewels. The organisms look like glass-jacketed worms with hairlike tentacles protruding from their heads. Although they are classified as plants, their appearance and behavior are closer to those of animals.

Apparently great colonies of these bugs become trapped

when the ice forms, yet continue to multiply as rapidly as ever; they actually live in microscopic caves which are found in ice so hard that an axe is required to cut it. The corethrons are among the most primitive of living things, slightly advanced forms of the one-celled algae which form the scum on stagnant water and which are quite abundant in the Antarctic. They propel themselves by a kind of jet propulsion and feel their way with their tentacles. Among them when the ice is melted are seen some tiny wormlike animals and microscopic crustaceans which supposedly feed on the glass-shelled plants.

The icy seas are full of surprises for biologists. One of the earliest discoveries of the Navy expedition was a colony of jet-propelled scallops, mollusks closely related to clams, floating among the ice cakes on the surface of water two miles deep. They were quite active. All scallops are light, thin-shelled animals whose jet propulsion mechanisms ordinarily enable them to rise only a few feet from the bottom mud where their lives are passed, and usually are found under shallow water, such as that over the Newfoundland banks. The existence of this colony raised speculations as to what strange creatures may exist in the abysmal depths of the Antarctic, of which virtually nothing is known.

Besides the acres of yellowish-brown the expedition biologists found small patches of living green ice—quite literally ice foliage. There was no evidence of the all-essential pigment chlorophyll in the corethron colonies first studied. The green ice, however, was formed by very similar organisms and the indication is that the pigment is formed from other chemicals in the bodies of the "bugs" when the sun returns; the living ice may be like a forest, turning green in summer and brown in winter.

Antarctic waters abound in fishes, most of them quite conventional in form and ways of life. Among the unusual forms, however, are black-eyed, transparent white heads with tiny tails attached to them which were fished from deep waters of the Ross Sea. Attached to each head was a pair of coal-black fins. The entire animal was about an inch long. These were fish, although possibly infantile forms of more conventional types. Other tiny fish brought up in plankton nets were inch-long eels which seemed to have no heads at all. There were great numbers of them and they may constitute an important part of the diet of whales.

Most of the fish found in south polar waters, according to the Navy survey and the surveys of the British *Discovery* expeditions, belong to the genus Notothenia. Some species, dull green in color and from six to eighteen inches long, resemble small rock cod; they are found near the bottom in shallow—sometimes in moderately deep—water, and are edible. The largest species reaches a length of three feet and is peculiar in that it swims near the surface, feeding on the crustacea which also serve as the chief food for whales.

Great pink fields of these crustacea, or krill, are tossed in the Antarctic seas. They are bright, shiny shrimps about two inches long, which multiply in uncountable number and are the principal consumers of the invisible diatoms; they make up the first superstructure of the Antarctic life pyramid. These krill fields seem to constitute biological entities as they drift passively with the currents. The shrimp are edible, and probably quite nutritious, but tasteless.

Shallow sea areas abound in a considerable variety of marine invertebrates, such as starfish, jellyfish, and squids. Small octopuses quite often are seen floating on the surface. Giant marine worms—one nearly two inches in diameter and twenty inches long with a loathsomely snake-like appearance—crawl over submerged rocks.

Naturalists have noted several species of the curious little insects known as springtails, which are found all over the world. One variety was noted by Dr. H. M. Bryant, biologist of the 1941 Byrd expedition, in trickles of water near snow banks. There usually were penguin rookeries near by. Springtails also were found under stones in frozen mud. As soon as thawing started they sprang to life. Says Dr. Bryant:

Trickles from melting snow would run together to form rivulets. These combined in turn to form tiny streams which ran into the sea. These small water courses all seemed to bear floating springtails. At the base of the rookery, where the little channels leveled out a bit before running under the ice, they collected in swarms so thick that they appeared as blotches of soot. It seemed at first as though they had collected accidentally in small back waters, but on closer observation it appeared that the swarms must occur by design or instinct. The flow of water had occurred during the first thaw of many days and at night, with the temperature again below freezing, the water drained away. The next morning the springtails were nowhere to be seen.

Mites are found more widely distributed. A common species is the "beetle mite" type, tough-skinned and slow-moving. It is found among certain lichens, upon which it apparently feeds. Dormant during the cold weather, it is awakened by the summer sun. Another species of mite is found among moss clumps; extremely fragile and fast-moving, it is visible only because of its bright red pigments. Two forms, one completely red and one with bright red appendages, are fairly common. These seem to be active when it is too cold for the beetle mites.

The most advanced form of insect life in the Antarctic is a wingless mosquito discovered by the Swedish explorer Nordenskjöld. Many rotifers, minute worms, have been observed in fresh water pools formed from melting snow, especially on the Palmer Peninsula, usually in January and February. Under favorable conditions the rotifers, usually red, form a scum on a pool bottom.

By far the most abundant form of fresh-water life is that of algae, one-celled plants which are nearly the most primitive of all living things. They first appear as yellowish green filaments in pools after about two weeks of thaw and soon are followed by blue-green types. They were so abundant in the fresh water lakes of the so-called "oases" on the Wilkes Land coast that they tinted the waters blue, green, and red.

Higher forms of vegetation naturally are very scarce on the continent and are found only in a few moist valleys protected from winds, or on narrow, ice-free coasts where the soil is exposed to the northern sun. Antarctic soil, where it can be found, appears fairly rich. Hyacinth bulbs were raised to blooming by Captain Scott and by the French explorer, Dr. Charcot. The latter also cultivated cress and onions. Sea kale seed planted in mossy soil near McMurdo Sound sprouted, but cold weather stopped further growth.

Mosses and lichens are quite abundant, especially on bare rock faces with a northern exposure; nearly fifty species of lichens were found on top of Mount Helen Washington in the Edsel Ford Mountains. Mosses are by far the predominant vegetation, sometimes covering areas of nearly an acre where bird guano supplies a semblance of soil. They appear to have a very high resistance to cold.

Any plant or animal which can survive in Antarctica must have enormous vital energy. Today this is expended in keeping a toehold on mere existence; once conditions became more favorable much of it would be diverted to spread and diversification. It might not be many generations, once the icecap started to melt rapidly, before the dead land's shores would be masses of blossoms in January and insect swarms become, as is now the case in the Arctic, nearly unendurable.

Today's Explorers

Antarctic exploration now is in its fourth major stage. The first was that of the sealers and whalers—Palmer, Weddell, Pendleton, Powell, and the rest—in the eighteen twenties. They proved the existence of the polar continent and little more.

The second was that of well-equipped government expeditions—Wilkes, Ross, D'Urville—in the eighteen forties. These men roughly determined the coastline, making it possible for Antarctica to be represented on maps.

The third was the glorious and tragic search for the South Pole—the expeditions of Scott, Shackleton, and Amundsen—in the first decade of the twentieth century.

A generation passed during which interest in the Antarctic was nearly non-existent. It was succeeded by the present era of accurate and detailed exploration by plane—the work of Rear Admirals Richard E. Byrd and Richard H. Cruzen, Sir Hubert Wilkins, Lincoln Ellsworth, and Finn Ronne.

For all Americans the name most closely associated with the land and seas around the South Pole is that of the world's foremost living explorer and one of the greatest explorers of all time, Admiral Byrd. For more than twenty years Antarctica has been the major interest of this outstanding flyer, navigator, geographer, mystic, and philosopher.

He has led four large expeditions into the Antarctic. He has flown twice across the pole and penetrated the mysterious land beyond, the vast unknown waste of the plateau which lies between the bottom of the earth and the Weddell Sea. Admiral Byrd has added more details to the geography of Antarctica than all his predecessors together. More than a quarter of the continent bears, and is likely to retain, the name Marie Byrd Land, after his wife. Some of his exploits rank among history's most noteworthy examples of human courage and endurance.

Before his first Antarctic adventure Byrd had made a notable place for himself in the history of aviation. He was the first man to fly over the North Pole; he was one of the first to fly over the Atlantic. Back in New York after the latter exploit, which came close to a tragic ending, he started work at once on a project which he had formulated while talking with Amundsen at Spitsbergen —a flight over the South Pole. He estimated the cost of an expedition at 750,000 dollars—a hard sum to raise, even in the lush days of the late twenties. He succeeded in raising about two-thirds of the required amount and started out with two ships, the *City of New York* and the *Eleanor Bolling,* five planes, ninety-five husky dogs, a snowmobile and large stores of food, radio equipment, and clothing. He was prepared to spend a year in the Antarctic.

The expedition reached the Bay of Whales, Amundsen's old base, shortly after Christmas, 1928, and a camp was set up on the ice—the first Little America. Byrd made his first flight over the pole on November 28, 1929, with a crew of three: pilot Bernt Balchen, radio operator Harold A. June, and Captain Ashley McKinley, aerial photographer. They discovered and mapped more than 400,000 square miles of the white continent, including the Edsel Ford and Rockefeller mountains east of the Ross Sea. For his flight over the pole Byrd was made a Rear Admiral by special act of Congress.

Four years later he was back in the Antarctic with his second privately financed and organized expedition for which, in the middle of the depression, it had been much more difficult to raise money. He was able to obtain only about 150,000 dollars in cash and supplies, some of which was forthcoming only with promises to endorse products in radio broadcasts.

During this second expedition the Admiral nearly lost his life. On March 28, 1934, he passed command of the base camp over to Dr. Thomas C. Poulter of the scientific staff and established himself alone in a shack sunk in the ice of the Ross Shelf, ninety miles south of Little America. There he remained alone through five months of the winter night, making daily meteorological observations. He was overcome by carbon monoxide and became too weak to turn the crank of the hand generator of his radio set. When finally rescued his life hung in the balance for some days.

His third Antarctic expedition, 1939–41, was sponsored by the government—the U. S. Antarctic Service was set up as a bureau of the Interior Department. A base was established on the same site as that which had been occupied by the second expedition and a second was set up far to the east off the coast of the Palmer Peninsula. Extensive air and coastal surveys were carried out.

With the end of World War II, in which he had rendered distinguished and highly confidential services, Admiral Byrd pressed for a fourth expedition on a scale which would dwarf all the others. This finally resulted in Operation High Jump, with twelve Navy ships, nearly four thousand officers and men, and some of the finest equipment developed by the Navy during the war. The group was under the operational command of Rear Admiral Richard H. Cruzen who had accompanied Byrd as an icebreaker commander on the U. S. Antarctic Service Expedition. This was by far the largest expedition ever to enter the Antarctic and its contributions were in proportion to its magnitude.

On this expedition Admiral Byrd made his second flight across the South Pole. He still dreams of going "beyond the pole" toward the Weddell Sea. He believes that the unseen stretches of the polar plateau are continuations of the featureless, undulating plain of ice already seen, though he does not exclude the possibility of there being great mountain ranges and ice-free valleys, warmed by some sort of subterranean furnace, where at least a low order of life will be found. Such, at least, is the dream of one of the profoundest dreamers of his generation, who makes his dreams into realities.

The notable contributions to Antarctic geography of two other explorers of the air age—Lincoln Ellsworth and Sir Hubert Wilkins—have been somewhat overshadowed by the accomplishments of Admiral Byrd. Ellsworth's best-known exploit was his flight from the base of the Palmer Peninsula to Little America in January, 1936; as a result of this 2,340-mile flight he laid claim to eighty thousand square miles for the United States and gave the name of his father, James W. Ellsworth, to approximately 250,000 square miles. This is the region, inland from the Sea of Bellingshausen, in which American territorial claims probably could be best sustained.

In the course of this flight Ellsworth made four intermediate landings and at one time was "holed in" by weather for eight days. When his radio failed he was completely out of touch with the world for twenty-two days before being rescued at the Bay of Whales by a British ship.

Commander of two Antarctic expeditions and closely associated with Ellsworth as technical advisor on three others is Sir Hubert Wilkins, best known as an Arctic explorer. He covered by air a considerable area at the foot of the Palmer Peninsula to which he gave the name of Hearst Land, after his sponsor, William Randolph Hearst.

A long stretch of the mountain-rimmed coastline remained unknown and it held one of the dead world's best-hidden secrets: Was Antarctica a single land mass? For a half-century geographers had advanced the thesis that it might essentially be bisected by a wide strait between the Weddell and Ross seas. The solution lay in the succession of ice-covered peaks that tower over the Weddell Ice Shelf.

The question was answered in the Antarctic summer of 1947 by Commander Finn Ronne. He had served as an officer on two of Admiral Byrd's expeditions, and his father had trekked to the pole with Amundsen. He went ashore on March 12, 1947, with a party of twenty-three —including Mrs. Ronne, the first woman ever to step on land in the Antarctic, on Stonington Island in Marguerite Bay at the foot of the western coast of the Palmer Peninsula. A winter night was spent in preparation for intensive exploration as soon as the sun returned.

Flights were made down both the west and east Palmer Land coasts. To the southwest the extension of the mountain chain was followed to where it terminated in a gradually rising, snow-covered plateau. To the southeast the hundred-foot-high ice shelf that fronts the Weddell Sea was followed for 450 miles. Altimeter readings on this flight convinced Ronne that Antarctica is a single continent. No evidence of a depression which would indicate a water channel under the ice was found—quite to the contrary, there was a constant rise in altitude. Altogether the party covered a conservative total of 250,000 square miles never before seen by man. Another 450,000 square miles was accurately photographed for the first time.

Flying Over Antarctica

The key to the mysteries of Antarctica appears to be the airplane, with which several thousand square miles of the great unknown can be surveyed tentatively in a few hours. The pilots of Admiral Byrd's 1946–47 expedition, for example, saw fleeting glimpses of approximately 1,700,000 square miles, more than a million of which had never before been crossed by man. They mapped 5,400 miles of coast, 1,400 completely unknown; the other four thousand miles had been seen only as a confusion of reality and mirage or through fog and drifting snow, so that its representation on charts was far from accurate.

Admiral Byrd's men discovered a total of twenty-two hitherto unknown mountain ranges, twenty-six islands, nine bays, twenty glaciers, and five capes never seen before. The ranges included literally hundreds of new mountains. From the seventy thousand photographs taken during their flights it has been possible to construct a new map detailing about one-third of the continent, though the other two-thirds remains virtually unknown. The geographical contributions were almost equivalent to the total made by all explorers of the past.

Any flight over the dead land, however rewarding, is highly perilous. The Navy and Marine Corps transport pilots and navigators who came south with Admiral Byrd were experienced in flying through flak fields and over trackless oceans in the South Pacific. The heavy R4D land planes and the patrol bomber sea planes furnished them were types with which they long had been familiar, but none of the men, except the commander of the group based at the Bay of Whales under the Admiral's personal supervision, had had previous experience in polar navigation, or any concern with polar regions. The exception was Commander William M. Hawkes, an air veteran of Alaska campaigns with an intense interest in the Antarctic springing from his boyhood reading of the exploits of men like Scott and Shackleton.

They were to explore the dead continent by a new method, the major technique of which was tri-metragon photography—a development of the science of photogrammetry which had come late in the war. Five cameras were mounted on each plane: one was pointed straight down, two were pointed downward at an angle of 30 degrees from the horizontal—thus essentially sweeping the ground below from horizon to horizon; a fourth was set to photograph various recording devices, including a clock, in the plane itself, and a fifth formed part of the radio altimeter apparatus which, by means of radio pulse echoes, continuously recorded the altitude of the plane above the ground. All five cameras were operated by an automatic device which clicked them simultaneously several times a minute, the frequency depending on the speed of the plane, its altitude, and the diversity of the landscape below.

Calculations showed that a plane equipped with such a battery could photograph in rough fashion about fifty thousand square miles in six hours—about the duration of a 750-mile flight inland and return—under ideal conditions. It was planned that on each flight two planes would fly parallel courses sixty miles apart, so that their photographs would overlap and could be checked against each other. When especially interesting features, such as mountains, lakes, or glaciers were found special missions were to fly low over the territory and obtain pictures showing greater detail.

Everything depended, of course, on good weather for planes and cameras. This rarely was found. It was highly mechanized, microscopic exploring, the greater part of which was done in a comfortable photo-interpretation laboratory weeks afterwards.

Once a plane rose from the ski strip at Little America it was virtually imprisoned in the sky for at least five hours; it could come down only with a crash landing on the rough ice surface, which would almost certainly ruin the aircraft itself and seriously endanger the crew. This was because the planes were, of necessity, badly overloaded. For a projected twelve-hour flight they carried a minimum load of about 29,000 pounds, although they were designed for only 25,000 pounds. Much of this extra load was made up of 1,600 gallons of gasoline weighing about six pounds to the gallon and consumed in flight at a rate of better than a hundred gallons an hour. Approximately six hours were required for lightening the load to the landing maximum.

Nor was there any way of jettisoning this gasoline. It was carried in two-hundred-gallon tanks, each of which weighed about twelve hundred pounds—altogether too much for the crew to handle. All the equipment, with the exception of the cameras whose weight made little difference, was firmly secured and could not be detached.

The planes had been stripped of every possible pound, even to some relatively vital equipment. Ways to decrease the weight had been the subject of many anxious conferences between Admiral Byrd and Commander Hawkes on the way to the Antarctic. These aircraft, of course, had not been designed for polar exploration, but they met the requirements best of any the Navy had available.

Even when a plane returned from a mission with its gasoline virtually exhausted the weight was so great that it could land only at the dangerous speed of about eighty miles an hour. The great weight also seriously restricted the altitude to which these planes could rise. At any place over the continent, it must be remembered, the minimum flying height was about twelve thousand feet above sea level, or approximately a half-mile over the surface of the névé. It was impossible to soar over a high mountain range which might unexpectedly loom ahead; some pass must be found. The pilots flew many miles through rock and ice canyons in the sky with solid black and white walls towering far above them on both sides, from which there was no escape in any direction but straight ahead.

It was also usually impossible to rise above a storm. Accurate weather prediction was important, yet—because so little is known of Antarctic meteorological conditions—virtually impossible. Storms rose and pilots found themselves in an inferno of tempest-tossed clouds with almost no warning. Missions were sent out to cover assigned routes along which, it appeared to the forecasters, good conditions would be found. But within an hour progress in the assigned direction might be completely blocked off by zero visibility. It would be futile to return to the base before the required amount of gasoline had been consumed, so the only answer was to fly in any direction in which the weather seemed clear, dodging and circling storms and looming mountains of clouds. Sometimes this proved an advantage, leading to surveys of areas which otherwise would not have been covered.

This operation was the first experience with large, land-based planes in the Antarctic. From the start the problem of a suitable airstrip on the névé proved a serious one. Efforts to lay down a metal strip, ready-made in sections, of the same general type as had proved successful in the African desert, soon were abandoned; the best that could be done was a runway of close-packed snow. The drawbacks were obvious when the first aircraft landed—taxiing planes froze to the strip if they paused for even a few seconds. All were equipped with skis through which wheels protruded, making possible both deck takeoffs and snow landings.

Wheels proved worthless in the snow; they broke through the hard upper crust, and often the skis broke through after them. Several days were lost removing the wheels altogether, but even then the skis froze to the runway in a few seconds—so solid that it often required twenty-five men to rock them loose. Finally the problem was solved fairly satisfactorily by parking the planes on a platform of boards coated with crude oil.

The overloaded planes could be got off the ice only with the aid of JATO—jet-assisted takeoff—bottles attached to the wings, which were jettisoned as soon as a craft was in the air.

Convenient fictions of the cartographer by which the navigator is able to fix his position on the map become more and more difficult to use as one approaches the pole, where the ordinary tools of navigation are unreliable. The south magnetic center lies, as does everything else on earth, to the north. Because of its proximity, however, the magnetic compass becomes erratic. The sky is covered with such thick clouds much of the time that no sun sights can be taken. There are no radio beacons within five thousand miles, and even the gyrocompass becomes quite untrustworthy.

The navigator must rely almost entirely on dead reckoning. It is natural enough that there should be mistakes in location of as much as 2 or 3 degrees—this is especially true with men whose previous navigational experience has been with the aids of modern science.

Few problems press harder for complete solution at present than that of air navigation in polar regions, with the Arctic basin almost certain to become the great sky road between the Eastern and Western hemispheres both in commerce and war. It is essential to invent new space-time artifacts.

The world literally is turned topsy-turvy in a new map system which was tested on these flights. A series of charts had been prepared especially for the expedition by the Navy's Hydrographic Office, where North and South poles were placed deliberately on opposite sides of the earth at the equator. The 180th meridian, the international dateline which passes through the Ross Sea, was combined with the meridian of Greenwich to become the equator.

This system is known as "inverse Mercator." Nearly all familiar maps are drawn according to the so-called Mercator projection, a device for picturing what actually is a curved surface on a flat surface. It results in great distortions of the polar areas. Greenland, for example, usually is shown about half the size of the United States, although actually it is less than one-third as large.

There is relatively little distortion in middle latitudes. Navigation in the neighborhood of the equator is almost as simple as if the earth really was a flat surface and great circles were straight lines. But in high latitudes navigation by such maps becomes extremely complicated and difficult, especially in a fast-moving plane. The sides-up earth maps, on the contrary, distort the figures of islands and continents near the actual equator, while the polar areas appear in their proper perspectives. Such maps, with the North Pole in Brazil and the South Pole in Borneo, were developed late in the war for air navigation near the North Pole by Canadian Royal Air Force pilots.

In the Antarctic air navigation is much more difficult than in the Arctic, due to the almost complete absence of any landmarks. Over the Ross Sea or the polar plateau pilot and navigator see below them only a monotonous white desert hour after hour. Even over the mountains they are little better off, for these are poorly described and, even when they can be identified, are poorly located on existing maps. It is generally admitted that piloting any sort of plane over the frozen seas at the top of the world would be relatively easy for a man who has had experience above the trackless wastes of ice at the bottom of the world. Even with good flying conditions experienced Navy pilots sometimes became seriously confused and found their way back to the air strip at Little America more by instinctive sense of direction than by scientific navigation.

One of the purely utilitarian purposes of the expedition was to test aviation accessories, such as fuels and lubrication oils, under high-altitude, cold-weather conditions which could not be found elsewhere in the world and to build up the nucleus of a corps of transport pilots expert in polar navigation problems. Rear Admiral Byrd, who directed all the flights and personally accompanied several of them, probably has more experience in this field than any other man living and his counsel often proved invaluable.

The experience of being lost over the white waste of the Antarctic is one of the most alarming imaginable. It happened to one crew on its first flight from the airplane carrier near Scott Island, at the northern edge of the ice pack, six hundred miles from Little America. All the navigational aids, by which radio guidance could be obtained from the expedition's ships, failed; the antenna had fouled with the landing gear on the takeoff. The plane was buried in a dense white fog of ice crystals in which there was no visibility, and it was impossible to rise above this fog for a possible sight of the sun. The two magnetic compasses aboard pointed in precisely opposite directions.

Major Robert R. Wier, the officer in command of the aircraft, said:

I have had more than 2,300 hours of flying since joining the Marines in 1941. Some 1,500 of them were over the southwest Pacific. I've never been scared, except once. Two hours in that white fog was enough to make up for all the 2,300 of complete freedom from fear. The six men in the plane had no way of knowing whether they were flying north or south. If the former, they were certainly doomed. There was not a possible landing place within three thousand miles. They were bound to dive eventually into the rough, icy sea. If their direction was south sooner or later they would be over the ice shelf where they could land with some hope of rescue. Brief glimpses downward through holes in the fog showed open water when, from the directions they had received, they should have been over pack ice. This was a strong indication that somehow the direction of the flight had become reversed and that they were back north of Scott Island, moving rapidly to their doom. But they could not quite believe this. An instinctive sense of direction told them they were on the right course. A conference was held and they decided to trust this instinct rather than the evidence of their eyes.

"There was no east, no west, no north, no south, no forward, no backward," said Navigator Raymond J. Butters, a Marine captain. "The magnetic compasses were swinging over the entire 360 degrees. Ice had formed over our wings, making it impossible to gain altitude above the fog where we could fix our position from the sun. Everybody else sees the sun every day and thinks nothing of it. Now to see it for half a second might mean the difference between life and death."

In the plane was an emergency radio set, intended to be set up on the ice in case of a forced landing far from the base. This depended on an aerial wire held aloft by a kite and the only way it could be used in an aircraft was in reverse, suspended downward. At first this seemed impossible since the wire became tangled in the landing gear every time it was tried, but finally the aerial was weighted with a beer bottle.

A continuous distress signal was sent out to Little America. It was never received. Suddenly a great wall of ice a hundred feet high appeared below. This could be only one thing—the Ross Barrier—for the plane had been flying an almost straight course south. Somewhere near the edge of this wall was Little America, but Wier and Butters did not know in which direction. If they had known they had no means of distinguishing east and west. They had to make a decision, however, and stick to it— probably for life or death—and they turned purely by instinct. The tent city came in sight just as a search plane was being warmed up to enter the bowl of milky darkness on a blind hunt for them.

Who Owns the Antarctic?

Antarctica, says the United States State Department, belongs to nobody.

This policy was expressed by Secretary Charles Evans Hughes in 1924 when he was asked whether the vast expanse of Wilkes Land could be taken under the Stars and Stripes by Presidential proclamation. He answered: "It is the opinion of this department that the discovery of lands unknown to civilization, even when coupled with the formal taking of possession, does not support a valid claim of sovereignty unless the discovery is followed by actual settlement of the discovered country."

At that time American claims to Wilkes Land would have been based on somewhat debatable evidence of discovery alone; there was only the shadowiest notion of its coastline.

Secretary Hughes was speaking of a dead world in which, it is probable, there never can be any bona fide "settlement." The policy has remained unchanged. The United States never has recognized any claims of its own citizens or of anybody else. It has, however, in communications with foreign governments, reserved all rights that it or its citizens may have in the Antarctic. American explorers, especially Admiral Byrd who is convinced that the continent contains mineral resources that may eventually prove valuable natural assets, have been loath to accept the dictum at its face value. Wherever the Admiral has gone he has insisted on accurate fixing of positions and the making of detailed maps, especially of coastlines. The records have been deposited in Washington as evidence either of American discovery or first scientific exploration, upon which future claims might be based. Following the 1946-47 expedition, for example, the United States might lay claim to much of Wilkes Land for the first time with at least an elementary knowledge of what territory it was claiming. The coast was found to have only a vague resemblance to anything pictured on maps in the past.

The United Kingdom, New Zealand, Australia, Norway, France, Argentina, and Chile all claim a big slice of the dead continent. The territory which Great Britain maintains under the rule of its Colonial office is the so-called Falkland Islands Dependencies, comprising all the continent and the sub-Antarctic islands between west longitudes 20 and 80, and extending in a great pie-shaped wedge to the South Pole. This includes all the possibly habitable section now known.

The "dependencies" are divided into two main groups, one including the large island of South Georgia and the South Orkney and Sandwich Island groups, the other the South Shetlands, the Palmer Peninsula, and a part of Coats Land, or the eastern shore of the Weddell Sea.

Separate postage-stamp overprints are issued for these areas. The claims rest on discovery, exploration, semi-permanent occupation, and actually carrying out some of the functions of government. They were asserted in letters patent issued by the Colonial Office on July 1, 1908, claiming all this territory as a dependency of the Falkland Islands and placing it under the authority of the crown-appointed governer of that colony. Further letters patent were issued in 1917, defining the boundaries.

Some of the British discovery claims may be debatable; however, the Royal Hydrographic Office was certainly the first to direct systematic surveys or prepare maps. For thirteen years, between 1926 and 1939, annual scientific expeditions were sent out by the Colonial Office. In the waters around these coasts the British carried out some of the most extensive deep sea investigations ever undertaken. This work, interrupted for a time by the war, was resumed in 1943 on a somewhat different basis—to make a complete survey of the Palmer Peninsula (called by the British Graham Land). There has been an exploring party on the continent ever since. Its presence, for some reason, was a top secret during the war years. Present plans call for permanent occupation of at least one station, but with changes of personnel every two or three years.

During the heyday of whaling between 1910 and 1930 a Falkland Islands magistrate spent three months every summer at Deception Island, the volcanic ring which was the headquarters of Yankee sealers a century ago. It is considered the natural "capital" of the dependencies. Thus there was an actual enforcement of British law—

about as good a basis for a territorial claim as can be found.

There are, however, two conflicting claims—those of Chile and Argentina. They conflict both with the British and with each other and both appear to have considerable validity. These claims now are being buttressed by permanent establishments.

Chile asserts her title to the territory from longitude 53 to 90 west, from the Strait of Magellan to the South Pole. To this territory she has given the name O'Higgins Land, after her national liberator. It includes most of the Palmer Peninsula to the Sea of Bellingshausen, and the Shetland Islands. Two bases are being maintained, largely as meteorological stations; one is Camp O'Higgins, near the southernmost point of the west coast of Palmer Land, the other is Camp Soberania in the South Shetlands.

The claim is based primarily on historical considerations. When Chile won her independence from Spain she acquired by treaty with the mother country all the territory which had been considered part of the colony. Spain had laid claim to all the unknown southland extending as far as the South Pole in 1539 and for more than two centuries her rights were never disputed.

Weather stations in the Antarctic today are as essential to Chile as are those in the Arctic to Canada and the United States, for a great deal of Chile's weather comes directly from the South Pole. Antarctic stations might even have some possible military significance to the republic in case of a world conflict in which she was actively involved, and the question of need is important in considering claims for unoccupied territory. There also is the possible basis of contiguity, generally admitted for Arctic lands but never for the Antarctic. Chile is the nearest of all independent powers to the Antarctic—both geographically and geologically, in fact, Palmer Land might be considered an extension of the Chilean mountains.

Argentina's claims are to the territory reaching as far as the pole between longitudes 25 and 74 west, including a good deal of the Weddell Sea. She also is maintaining two permanent bases, one in the South Orkney Islands and one on Deception Island at longitude 52.56 west. This island, discovered by Nathaniel Palmer in 1820, long was the headquarters of Yankee sealers and is probably the best-known spot in the Antarctic.

The Argentine claims are based on precisely the same arguments as those of Chile. Settlement of the conflict presumably will rest on reinterpretation of old Spanish treaties.

The British-Chilean-Argentine dispute flared briefly in 1948, when the three nations mutually agreed to make no naval demonstrations in the Antarctic and to send no warships south of latitude 60; all three were to respect each other's scientific expeditions. This arrangement may continue indefinitely, or until the Palmer Land area becomes of vital importance to some one of the contenders.

In 1923 the region lying between approximately longitudes 150 west and 160 east was assigned by the British government to New Zealand. This so-called Ross Dependency includes both eastern and western shores of the Ross Sea and the Ross Shelf. For exploration it is the most significant area in Antarctica but it is, of course, uninhabitable by any but exploring parties. New Zealand, to date, has been unable to exercise any of the functions of sovereignty but formally protested, to keep the record clear, against the presence of the American Navy expedition at the Bay of Whales.

The largest, and least known, of all the Antarctic areas, from longitude 160 to 45 east, was claimed by Australia in 1933. France, however, previously had asserted sovereignty over a small area around longitude 140 east, known as Adélie Land. This claim was based on the discoveries of the French explorer, Captain Dumont D'Urville, in 1840, and was not disputed by the Australians. The French showed great interest in the American discoveries along its coast and since have established an expedition there; they evidently have no idea of abandoning their claims.

Most of the Australian quadrant lies directly south of that continent and the principal exploration there, up to the present, has been that of the Australian explorer, Sir Douglas Mawson. The government had planned to establish a permanent station on the coast but this was prevented by the outbreak of the war.

Japan, up to her collapse as an empire, had vague claims which might have included anything from the entire continent to a small part of the Ross Shelf. In the winter of 1912 Lieutenant Choku Shirase of the Japanese Navy led a sledge trek about 160 miles southeastward from the Bay of Whales. He had started out for the South Pole, but Scott and Amundsen were already on their way there. Shirase stopped in the middle of the shelf, raised the Japanese flag, and named the place "Yamoto Sestrugen—" Japanese snow plain. The Japanese also made a few landings along the coast but did not venture more than ten miles inland.

The emperor never tried seriously to assert the claims of Shirase, who died in the last year of World War II at the advanced age of eighty-six, but they were held in reserve as a possible basis for whaling rights in the Antarctic. Japanese whalers were the first to return to the old hunting grounds in the winter of 1947, by special permission of General MacArthur, and two of their ships maintained cooperative weather stations with the American Navy.

The flag of Norway was the first to fly over the South Pole. The country, because of her great whaling industry, has a greater economic interest than any other nation in the seas and lands below the circle, but it was not until January, 1939, that she made a formal claim to continental territory. Then King Haakon proclaimed under the Norse flag all the area "extending from the limits of the Falkland Islands Dependencies in the west to the limits of the Australian Antarctic Dependency in the east [45 east longitude], with the land lying within this coast and the environing seas." The whole was called Queen Maud Land. Previously two little islands—Bouvet, south of Africa, and Peter I Island in the Bellingshausen Sea on the other side of the continent—had been proclaimed under Norwegian sovereignty "to give the whaling industry in that region points of support and to guard it against possible encroachment on the part of foreign powers."

Norway staked its claim to the vast continental area, previously unclaimed by anybody, only when German planes began to fly over it with the avowed intention of making it a part of Hitler's empire. The region was, and still is, about the least-known part of the continent; it was not until 1929 that the first explorers reached the mainland in this part of the Antarctic. In the summer of that year the eminent Norwegian whaler Lars Christensen dispatched an expedition under the command of Captain Riiser-Larsen which photographed from the air what now is known as the Princess Martha Coast. A second expedition sent out by Christensen in the winter of 1930-31 discovered and explored by plane the present Princess Ragnhild Coast. In 1935 still another Christensen expedition made extensive air explorations in the same area. These discoveries alone were enough to give the Norwegians a valid claim, even if Amundsen had not entitled the kingdom to a big slice of almost any part of the continent. In 1929 she had entered into an agreement with Great Britain not to raise any claim to land within the region which had been brought under British dominion.

The seas off these coasts were of capital importance to the Norwegian whaling industry and the factory ships sometimes come quite close to the edge of the ice pack. A question that may have an important bearing on the freedom to be extended whaling expeditions is the determination of the limit of territorial waters. The British always have maintained that the pack ice must be considered part of the continent, have assumed that it generally reaches as far north as the 60th parallel, and have required whalers operating off the territories they claim to pay for licenses.

Admission of the Norwegian claims leaves one large

sector a no-man's-land: the territory lying between the 150th and 170th west meridians, south of the Bellings-hausen and Franklin D. Roosevelt seas. It includes most of the country which has been explored by Admiral Byrd and Lincoln Ellsworth. Essentially all exploration in this area has been by Americans, so a United States claim to this territory presumably would involve little diplomatic difficulty. Of all Antarctica this segment is probably the most difficult of access for a landing party and its vast interior remains almost entirely a mystery.

Hitler had his eye on Antarctica, but he got there too late. Steel-barbed swastikas rained upon more than 600,000 square miles of the white continent the stormy winter before the war. A region of black mountain peaks and ice plains, extending 20 degrees of longitude east and west of the meridian of Greenwich south of the Weddell Sea, was named New Schwabia. It represented the most systematic effort yet made to establish a south polar empire —"to secure for Germany her share in the approaching division of the Antarctic among world powers and thus to create the basis for her right to continue and develop her whaling industry."

The 1938-39 cruise of the steel-belted catapult ship *Schwabenland* under the command of Dr. Alfred Ritscher is of particular significance in that it largely initiated the present-day techniques of polar exploration and provided essentially the only geographic data on what lay beyond the coastline of the Antarctic Continent south of Africa. The region falls mostly within territory now claimed by Norway.

Dr. Ritscher and his men worked with customary German thoroughness. The *Schwabenland* proceeded southward through leads in the pack to within less than fifty miles north of the continental coast, where thick ice made further progress impossible. From this line seaplanes were catapulted by compressed air from the flight deck to make long incursions over the continent across the ice-cliffed Princess Martha and Princess Astrid coasts.

This was Germany's major effort in Antarctic exploration. Two previous expeditions under the flag of the Reich had been ice-foiled. The last, that of the *Deutschland* in 1911–13 commanded by the veteran Arctic explorer and scientist Wilhelm Filchner, also was in the Weddell Sea area. Filchner had encountered and traced westward for 120 miles a great ice wall from fifty to a hundred feet high which blocked all access to the land. It seemed in every way analogous to the Ross Barrier on the other side of the continent. The *Deutschland* was caught in a flash freeze of the pack ice and drifted helplessly all winter. This expedition gave Germany an historic interest, and basis for some sort of territorial claims, in this part of Antarctica.

Ritscher's plane crews were provided with bundles of light metal shafts about two yards long and weighted with sharp, ten-inch spear points. At the other end were three stabilizing planes at right angles to the shaft, one of which had stamped on its surface the Nazi national insigne. Dropped from an altitude of 1,500 feet, it was found, these shafts would penetrate about three inches into the glacial ice and remain standing upright. This had been established by numerous tests over glaciers in the Alps. Several thousand of these were dropped.

This expedition introduced photogrammetry into polar exploration. The planes flew in rectangular courses over the edge of the continent. Theoretically about 200,000 square miles from horizon to horizon would be in range of the cameras on each flight. Actually as much as 65,000 square miles were photographed on a single mission. Dr. Ritscher claimed fairly reliable mapping of more than 350,000 square miles from 11,600 pictures and reliable observation of an additional 250,000 square miles.

The experience proved of considerable value to the Luftwaffe during the war. The techniques introduced were, with war-developed improvements, essentially the same as those used by the American Navy expedition on the other side of the continent eight years later.

As soon as striking natural features—mountains, glaciers, lakes and the like—were seen they were reported by radio to the *Schwabenland*, charted on maps, and given the names of officials of the Nazi government, their wives, eminent German scientists and the like. It was the primary purpose of the expedition that New Schwabia carry everywhere and unmistakably the stamp of the swastika. Many of these names, particularly those of members of the expedition, probably will be allowed to stand.

Altogether sixteen flights were made, mostly across the Princess Martha Coast which fronts the sea with precipitous green ice cliffs a hundred feet high. From these cliffs, the German pilots reported, the land rises in a series of rolling, snow-covered slopes to an elevation of about two thousand feet above sea level. Thence to the southward rise several ranges of high mountains. The topography, it appears from Dr. Ritscher's reports, is quite similar to that of the mountainous areas east and west of the Ross Sea mapped by the American Navy expedition in 1947. The German pilots also reported several large ice-free areas north of the mountains below "dead" glaciers. A few of these frozen lakes were photographed. These presumably are similar to the lake regions discovered by the Americans on the other side of the continent.

Regardless of conflicting claims, nobody is likely to go to war over Antarctica. The continent is not an available source of strategic materials at present. It was practically the only place on earth where there were no military operations during the last war. Unlike the north polar basis, it has no strategic or tactical value. The last world conflict reached only as far south as French-owned Kerguelen Island on the edge of the Antarctic, about halfway between South Africa and Australia.